the foodphysio

Eating My Way Back to Health

A Gluten & Dairy Free Recipe Book

By Louise & Richard Blanchfield

DISCLAIMER
This book is not intended to be used as medical advice. If you have any condition you should always consult with your doctor before you proceed with any self-management to ensure that you are safe to do so.
This book is published in good faith but neither the publisher or the author shall be held liable for any alleged damages arising from any suggestion or information contained in this book.

I dedicate this book to my family. They mean the world to me and their health and happiness is of the utmost importance.

foreword

To all those people who feel they are helpless and have nowhere else to turn, I want to say there is another way. You can help yourself, what you eat and the way you choose to live your life does make a difference. And even if you have a condition that may be life threatening you can still feel better by making some changes to enjoy the time you have left. Changing your diet and lifestyle gives you focus and allows you to take back some control. I believe that our bodies are amazing, if we fuel them well and allow them to be!

acknowledgments

Thanks to Josephine Blanchfield, Alison Brown, Alicia Campbell and Gareth Jones for proof reading and editing. Thanks to Graeme and Susan Drummond for the cookathon to test some of the quantities for the recipes.

contents

lunch 85

soups 85

light meals 100

main meals 115

our story

Hi, I am Louise, wife to Richard and mum of two children, Megan and Alec. I want to start by welcoming you to my new self-help and recipe book, which can help you to improve your diet in order to maximise your body's ability to feel as good as it can. Our bodies are always trying to heal themselves. All that we really need to do is to give them the best environment so that they can achieve this!

I have not always been interested in nutrition but, as a physiotherapist, I have always been aware of how fuelling your body correctly can influence performance and healing. This book details what my husband and I did to help his health, the food we ate and supplements that we used to help resolve his issues. Plus, it includes over a hundred recipes of food that we enjoyed along the way developed and written by Richard and I.

Our journey all started about 10 years ago when Richard developed pain in both of his shoulders. He asked me to take a look and I initially tried to treat him. However, it failed to respond to physiotherapy and, indeed, was slowly getting worse. To me the pain did not appear to be like it was a typical musculoskeletal pain. For example, it was constant from waking until going to bed. Activities made it worse but nothing made it better, it was not dependent on posture. He had swollen, hot joints that were quick to be irritated and very slow to ease, if at all. Even acupuncture failed to have any impact on the pain. I felt the pain was from some form of systemic inflammation.

By now it was severe in both shoulders, he could not raise either arm above 90 degrees (higher than horizontal in front of him) and he could not dress himself without help. A deep ache had started in his lower back, which he never seemed to be able to shift and was gradually wearing him down. Finally he agreed to go and see his GP, who took some blood tests and found that his inflammatory blood markers were high, so he was sent to see a rheumatologist.

By the time he got to see a rheumatologist things had taken a turn for the worse. He had developed episodes of pain fluctuating from his hip to his knee and back, each time lasting for 4 to 5 days and severe enough so that he could not walk without a stick. His joints, when in this state, were hot and swollen and kept him awake at night. He stopped being able to play with our son, then 3 years old. Even only 10 minutes with a bat and ball meant that he could not move his wrist for the next 3 to 4 days due to the resultant pain and swelling. And if his wrist was 'in flare' he could not eat with that hand, he could not drive or even do up his trousers! Not to mention, that from time to time, even his jaw would flare so that he couldn't chew anything.

Eventually he saw a consultant rheumatologist, who said, "No-one gets better, everyone gets worse and you could be in a wheelchair by the time you're 60". She measured nine spinal markers checking various ranges of movement as a record to be able to use to monitor his deterioration. She diagnosed a non-anchylosing spondylo-arthropathy (arthritis) and told him that it was secondary to another long-standing medical condition which he had had since he was eighteen, namely, his inflammatory bowel disease, ulcerative colitis. He was already on a strong anti-inflammatory medication for this daily and she quadrupled his dose. She told him that, if this did not work, the next drug to try was a nasty one, so to stay on this as long as possible.

Ulcerative colitis is similar to Crohn's Disease but colitis occurs lower down in the bowel and is considered to be an autoimmune disease. It involves inflammation of the cells which line the gut and results in flares when the disease is said to be 'active', giving symptoms of diarrhoea, blood and / or mucus in the stools and pain. At its worst, it can lead to having part of the bowel removed as symptoms can be very debilitating and result in large amounts of bleeding, fatigue, weight loss, fever and increased risk of cancer. Current medical treatment aims to treat the symptoms by decreasing inflammation or suppressing the immune response (explained later) but does not seek to correct the root problem, i.e. whatever may be causing the damaged and inflamed lining of the gut in the first place.

For Richard, it started when he was 18 and he was subsequently on medication for the next 20 years or so to control flare-ups of his condition. For the first 10 years he was on and off steroids until, in 1998, he ended up in hospital about to have part of his bowel removed. This was when the doctors tried him on a new drug. It was an immunosuppressant called azathioprine, and, sure enough it settled his flare and the surgery never happened. Roll forwards another 10 years and it was time to come off the drug due to an increased risk of developing blood cancers with continued use. This is where all of his real problems started to happen. The drug had suppressed his immune system and when he came off it, his immune system had a huge and aggressive rebound response. The inflammatory arthritis. However, this turned out to be far worse than his colitis symptoms had ever been.

The anti-inflammatory drug, of which the rheumatologist increased his dose, did not help. His flares were becoming more and more frequent and more intense. He could not play tennis, go swimming, play with the children or cook, which he loved to do. I could not accept that this was it. His life was going to be one long bout of pain that was going to steadily get worse. He already woke in the night crying because the pain was so bad, his flaring joints were hot and swollen to twice their normal size and he could not use them, at all. He could not get out of a chair without help, he was only 40. Our lives were on hold...

His GP was of little help, we went to discuss possible dietary changes that may improve his situation and were quite categorically told, "There are a lot of quack diets out there, just keep taking the medication".

So, we were on our own.

As a physiotherapist it is hard to watch anyone struggle with a physical problem and do nothing. As a wife it is even harder to watch your partner in pain struggling with the most basic of daily tasks. For me, there was no question that I could sit by and watch him continue like this, or even, just get worse and worse. So, being a physio and originally a neuroscientist, I set out to see what information was to be found which may be of use. I started trawling the internet, reading research papers, looking at forums, cross-referencing information and reading books. When the children went to bed I became glued to the computer. My aim was that if we could find out what was driving the inflammation in his system, maybe, just maybe we could at least halt the progression of his disease. Little did I know at that point that what we put into place would actually reverse it!

Finding the root cause of any problem is the key to resolving it. The primary aim for me was to investigate Richard's illness and determine what may be the likely causes. To find the cause of the arthritis I needed to look back at when he was 18 and had his first flare of ulcerative colitis. Something at that point in his life had triggered the disease to start.

If you look at the NHS website it says that the cause of colitis is unknown. It says that it could be:

- "The immune system mistakes 'friendly bacteria' in the colon as a harmful infection and attacks them resulting in an inflamed colon and rectum";
- "A viral or bacterial infection triggers the immune system but for some reason it doesn't turn off";
- "No infection is involved and the immune system just malfunctions by itself";
- "An imbalance between good and bad bacteria within the bowel";
- "There is a genetic component"; or
- "Environmental factors may play a role like air pollution, medication and certain diets".

It also says that, "Although no factors have so far been identified, countries with improved sanitation seem to have a higher population of people with the condition suggesting that reduced exposure to bacteria may be an important factor".

In America, doctors at The Institute of Functional Medicine postulate that colitis and Crohn's could be caused by, "Inappropriate immune responses to foods or commensal bacteria".

For Richard, possible connections to his development of the disease included:

- a family history of bowel problems (his mum had suffered with bowel cancer);
- 4 years of low dose antibiotics to treat acne in his early teens, which would have affected his gut bacteria;
- poor diet and drinking increased levels of alcohol whilst at university; and
- although this is not a cause of the disease, he has always internalised stress (a known trigger of flare-ups).

So it seemed logical to me that addressing his gut was the first thing to do. So I looked at:

- replenishing gut bacteria;
- removing foods that may cause inflammation;
- possible food sensitivities which could irritate his gut;
- increasing foods that reduce inflammation; and
- including foods which may help his gut to heal.

I also looked at how to reduce stress and better coping mechanisms (see later lifestyle chapter).

In essence, I switched our diets around, changed our lifestyles to improve our work/life balance and we ate a clean, wholefood diet. From my research I decided to make a variety of changes. The measures we took were:

- removed gluten as we thought this could be a food sensitivity (explained later);
- removed dairy as it is very inflammatory and could be a food sensitivity;
- put in foods to ensure good calcium intake;
- removed all processed food to make food easier for the body to digest;
- increased our fruit and vegetable intake to 8-10 per day to boost vitamin and mineral levels in our diet;
- juiced for breakfast to help increase the volume of vitamins and minerals that could be taken on board on a daily basis;
- increased oily fish intake to 3 per week, as they are very anti-inflammatory;
- ate no pork products or processed meat, as they are inflammatory; and
- gave Richard some supplements to speed things along a bit - a fish oil, curcumin (which is turmeric – very anti-inflammatory), a good probiotic and glutamine (fuel to help the gut repair).

Richard was the best 'control' subject ever because, to be honest, he thought it was a whole load of rubbish, but also thought, "It can't do any harm, it's all healthy food, so why not give it a go?" The eventual outcome, though, was amazing!

Within four weeks he noticed the pain in his shoulders and back was not quite as intense. Then he realised that the episodes of knee or hip pain were not as frequent, or lasted for less time when they were in flare. Over the following months, he slowly started to get less and less pain. We carried on with the diet. Juicing for breakfast, a salad or soup for lunch and either fish or meat for tea with loads of vegetables. We tried to stay as unprocessed as possible with the food that we ate. Even gluten-free products can be filled with chemicals and I did not believe these would help either.

After about nine months he had a review with the rheumatologist and confessed all. He told her that he had not been taking her anti-inflammatory medication and detailed all of the dietary changes which I had put in place and how he was feeling much better. After checking his sheet detailing all of the changes, she said, "I wish all of my patients would eat that way". She got blood tests to check that his calcium and vitamin D levels were okay and re-checked those nine spinal markers that recorded his range of movement when he had initially presented with his condition. Eight of them had improved! He asked her why she had not told him about possible dietary help when he had come before and she replied, "People usually only want to take a tablet".

We now had the doctor's agreement that what we were doing was fine, so we continued, and about six months later Richard went for his routine colonoscopy to check that his bowel health was good. After the test the consultant came round to discuss the results as usual and told Richard, "You have an entirely normal looking bowel'. So, Richard enquired about the scarring on his bowel from previous colitis attacks (which had been present since he was 18 years old), only to be asked by the consultant, "What scarring?" It had completely vanished!

I was amazed at how an unqualified person could use the internet to find out information to not only alleviate symptoms, but actually reverse years of damage from a chronic disease. It inspired me to go and get properly qualified in order to help others like Richard and, indeed, those with other problems too. I am constantly surprised and in awe at just what our bodies can do if we fuel them correctly. You do not have to 'just keep taking the tablet!'

Richard is now able to play tennis, goes swimming often, plays with our children pain-free and is back to enjoying his cooking again. He is totally medication-free as his colitis is in complete remission. His arthritis flares occasionally, if he falls off the dietary wagon or gets extremely stressed. He has his life back and that is worth everything to us. It is not as hard as you think to turn your diet around. Your health is the true wealth and food is the key.

This book details exactly what changes we made to help his body heal itself and, it goes one stage further, to include lots of recipes which we enjoyed along the way. Our aim now is to spread the word to as many people as possible, about just how changing your diet can have a huge impact on the way that you feel. We hope this helps you as much as it helped us, at a time when we felt that conventional medicine had no more to offer.

I am now the Food Physio, trained in both physiotherapy and nutritional therapy. I see a range of clients for either physiotherapy, nutritional therapy or, increasingly, a combination of the two. I also give talks to businesses and social groups on how you can change your life just by changing your diet and lifestyle!

how this book works

The initial quarter of the book discusses what dietary changes we made to help Richard's body heal itself. It can either be read in sections or as a whole, or even used as a reference book. It also includes some meal suggestions and an example of six days worth of meals. Although I have provided references, it is not intended as a text book, but more of a guide bringing together all that we did, at a time when I was not qualified, to help Richard's health. It does not go into great depth as, in fact, only very simple, basic changes were necessary to help his health improve, but please find the reference list at the end of the book if you would like to read more.

The main section of the book includes the recipes, which are all gluten- and dairy-free. They all detail their preparation time and how many of your fruit and vegetable quota for the day they give you. It includes how simple they are to make plus a taste tip on how to switch it around a bit and finally, each recipe includes its own 'back to health bonus'. The bonus section details how each particular recipe will benefit your health.

Symbol	Meaning
	Preparation Time
	Fruit and vegetable quota per portion
	Simplicity
	Taste Tip
	Back to Health bonus

digestion basics

So, now for the science bit. Let us start with a brief look at how your gut works, so that we know what we need for it to function well and, therefore, what it needs to help your body heal itself. You would not put the wrong fuel in a car, yet we put the wrong fuel in our bodies every day! We accept that our hair and eye colour are different from person to person so it is not too far a stretch to imagine that our guts are all different too, and what one person can eat and flourish on can be detrimental to another. There exists the phrase 'we are what we eat' and, what is actually more appropriate may be, 'we are what we absorb'. If our guts are not absorbing food correctly, no matter how good the diet is, we will not take on board the nutrients we need. So, gut health is crucial.

Our guts have numerous functions. They:

- provide us with the nutrients that we need to survive, i.e. they supply energy and nutrients for both repair and growth;

- remove waste from our system;

- help our metabolism to run well; and

- protect us from any dangerous organisms brought into our bodies via the mouth (immunity).

Imagine your gut as one long hose. When we chew food we are not only breaking it up until it is hopefully liquid (unless you rush and swallow food in chunks) but we are also mixing saliva around the food which starts off the digestion process. Saliva contains an enzyme called amylase that breaks down carbohydrates (bread, pasta, rice and most fruit and vegetables) into its individual glucose particles. After swallowing, food hits our stomach where we need high acid levels to break down protein (meat, fish, nuts, seeds, chickpeas, lentils) into amino acids before they are released into the bowel. High acid levels also kill off any dangerous bacteria on the food and are needed to release important vitamins like B12 from our food.

After exiting the stomach, food moves into the small intestine, where more enzymes are released to help break down the food further, and also bile is added to help split up any fat that we have eaten into fatty acids and glycerol. It is here where digestion is completed and nutrient absorption from our food occurs. The small intestine has finger-like projections on it called 'villi', increasing the surface area of the gut to maximise what it can absorb. These villi have cells along them that allow food, which has been broken down into small molecules such as glucose, amino acids or fatty acids, to be transferred into your bloodstream to be taken away and used in the body. The cells are held together by 'tight junctions'. Gut bacteria live in both the small and large intestine.

Once into the large intestine the body concentrates on removing fluid from the gut and forming a good stool. It is here where the majority of our gut bacteria live and exert their effects. If we have the right mix of bacteria, they help to break down any fibre from our food which has remained unchanged by digestion so far, and make enzymes and vitamins for us to absorb.

In order for our guts to function well we need:

- the right nutrients in our body to make the things for adding to the gut (digestive enzymes, stomach acid, bile);
- the fuel to help the gut cells work effectively and repair our bodies; and
- good bugs within the gut that provide the best environment for our food to be broken down (more about that later).

Our guts are performing well if we are opening them at least once per day. Constipation is defined as 'less than 1 stool per day'. If you are not opening your bowels daily, you are not cleaning waste from your body efficiently and, if a stool sits in your gut, used hormones and toxins waiting within it get reabsorbed back into the body. To make sure you are opening your bowels daily you need plenty of fibre (8-10 portions of fruit and vegetables per day), good hydration (6-8 glasses of water per day) and good levels of vitamin C (kiwis, peppers, oranges).

High sugar diets really slow the transit time of food through the gut so, if you are struggling with constipation, this must be your first objective: Get the sugar out, increase your water consumption and get more fibre in and you will see a difference in no time. If your gut does not respond to that, kiwis in particular are excellent to get you moving, as they contain both fibre and vitamin C whilst being low in sugar. Two a day will get a sluggish bowel moving.

Do not use laxatives regularly or even at all. The bowel starts to rely on them and becomes lazy so that, when you stop taking them, the bowel grinds to a halt. If you are stuck in this rut, then try taking psyllium husks as they are natural fibre, which bulks out your stool and helps to make your bowel work. The muscle in your bowel contracts around the food you put in. If there is more fibre there is more bulk so the muscle can more easily contract around it. Make sure you follow it down with a large glass of water though, as psyllium needs it to bulk properly and, if you do not drink enough, you will dehydrate yourself. I would recommend the tablets as I am told the powder is rather awful! Caution though, if you take medication you must get it checked first to make sure that psyllium does not alter the way your medication is absorbed into the body. You can also help the bowel to work more efficiently by having three main meals a day and no snacking. Larger meals give the smooth muscle plenty of bulk to contract around and promote easier transit through the gut.

When you do go to the loo it should be easy to pass the stool. If it is hard or the stool is cracked on its surface, then you are dehydrated or you are not eating enough fibre. It should be a smooth sausage shape, not little bits like rabbit poo or loose without form. If it is loose, it could be because you are flaring if you have inflammatory bowel disease, and should settle as the bowel becomes less inflamed. Alternatively, you could have an abundance of bad bacteria in your gut upsetting stool formation. Either way, putting in a gut healing programme like the one outlined further in this book should help.

top tip

Did you know?
Eating foods rich in vitamin C help you to absorb more iron, so if you are tired and think low iron could be the cause, get some orange on your spinach-based salad

finding the root

My research into colitis found an explanation for the development of colitis and other autoimmune conditions. It postulated that gut function can be altered by gluten and the presence of certain bacteria. Absorption of glucose, amino acids and fatty acids into the bloodstream from the gut occurs via cells on the villi which allow these small particles to diffuse through or actively transport them into the bloodstream. Larger undigested food molecules are not small enough to pass through the cells via these mechanisms. 'Tight junctions' hold these cells together to ensure that absorption has to occur through the cells. However, gluten stimulates the production of a protein called zonulin.

This regulates the integrity and permeability of tight junctions. If zonulin is produced, the breakdown of tight junctions is induced and causes them to effectively 'open' to leave a hole in between the cells of the gut. Hence, larger undigested food molecules can now pass through into the bloodstream. The immune system sees it as foreign and attacks it, producing antibodies. So now, you have antibodies in your bloodstream searching for gluten to attack. Whenever you eat more gluten, it produces more zonulin, which further opens the tight junctions. These remain open, instead of closing up overnight as they usually would when zonulin levels decrease. The gut is now considered to have holes in it and hence the term 'leaky gut' has come into use. This in turn results in more undigested food moving into the bloodstream, which is swiftly attacked by the immune system.

You now have a war raging in your body against gluten or whatever food has 'leaked' across. It could be dairy, tomatoes, anything. The immune response keeps happening, which causes more inflammation, and the now open tight junctions allow more undigested food through, so you can react to multiple foods. But, although you may react to multiple foods, they do not all increase zonulin production. They have merely leaked across as the tight junctions are already open and so they too elicit an immune response. This is why some food intolerance tests, done at the wrong time, can be misleading.

Everyone on the planet produces zonulin if they eat gluten. However, zonulin production is not sufficient to cause the tight junctions integrity to degrade as far as to allow food through past it in normal individuals. And, overnight, zonulin levels decrease (when no gluten is present) and the tight junctions regain their normal structure. Research has now confirmed that individuals with a variety of autoimmune conditions have excessive zonulin production and the levels remain higher for longer than in unaffected individuals. Therefore tight junction integrity is compromised to such a degree that they are unable to regain their structure overnight.

Some harmful bacteria can also increase the production of zonulin. We all have beneficial

and harmful bacteria present in our guts at all times, but usually the volume of harmful bacteria is insufficient to exert an effect on the gut. However, if your bacteria levels have been altered due to illness or the use of antibiotics, harmful bacteria levels can dramatically increase. This increased number now stimulate the release of zonulin in sufficient levels to affect tight junction integrity and so, once again leaky gut symptoms can be experienced. The increased zonulin production will continue until the bacteria is either killed off entirely or reduced to insignificant levels so that it can no longer exert an effect.

Some people suffer with a low level of irritation in the gut for years, which grumbles from time to time giving you indigestion, bloating, wind and occasional pain. Often we just put up with this, thinking it is normal or, if it worsens, we could end up at the GP's with a diagnosis of IBS (irritable bowel syndrome) or, it could go even further...

Everybody is different, so the immune reaction in the body will also be different. With some people the immune response will be more severe. An antibody identifies what it is going to attack because it looks for a marker on the surface of each substance that it encounters. These markers are made out of protein. If you have developed antibodies to gluten, your immune system now searches the body for protein markers similar to the one for gluten. If part of your joints or other structures in your body (e.g. thyroid, pancreas, gut, etc.) also have a similar protein marker on their surface, then these antibodies will also attack that part of your body. So, you now have your immune system attacking your body because it has confused your body with a foreign invader. Hence, you have developed an autoimmune, or inflammatory, response. There are many recognised autoimmune diseases, some of which are more surprising than others:

Acute disseminated encephalomyelitis
Addison's disease
Alopecia areata
Ankylosing spondylitis
Anti-glomerular basement membrane nephritis
Antiphospholipid syndrome
Autoimmune angioedema
Autoimmune hepatitis
Autoimmune inner ear disease
Autoimmune oophoritis
Autoimmune pancreatitis
Autoimmune retinopathy
Autoimmune thrombocytopenic purpura
Autoimmune thyroiditis

Autoimmune urticaria
Balo disease
Behçet's disease
Bullous pemphigoid
Coeliac disease
Chronic fatigue syndrome
Chronic inflammatory demyelinating polyneuropathy
Churg-Strauss syndrome
Cicatricial pemphigoid
Cogan syndrome
Cold agglutinin disease
Crest syndrome
Crohn's disease
Dermatitis herpetiformis

Dermatomyositis
Diabetes mellitus type 1
Discoid lupus erythematosus
Endometriosis
Eosinophilic esophagitis
Eosinophilic fasciitis
Erythema nodosum
Essential mixed cryoglobulinemia
Evans syndrome
Fibromyalgia
Giant cell arteritis
Goodpasture syndrome
Graves' disease
Guillain–Barré syndrome
Hashimoto's encephalopathy
Hashimoto thyroiditis
Henoch-Schonlein purpura
IgA nephropathy
IgG4-related systemic disease
Inclusion body myositis
Inflamatory bowel disease (ibd)
Interstitial cystitis
Juvenile arthritis
Kawasaki's disease
Lambert-Eaton myasthenic syndrome
Leukocytoclastic vasculitis
Lichen planus
Lichen sclerosus
Ligneous conjunctivitis
Linear IgA disease
Lyme disease (chronic)
Ménière's disease
Microscopic polyangiitis
Mixed connective tissue disease
Mooren's ulcer
Mucha-Habermann disease
Multiple sclerosis
Myasthenia gravis
Myositis
Neuromyelitis optica

Optic neuritis
Palindromic rheumatism
Paraneoplastic cerebellar degeneration
Parry-Romberg syndrome
Parsonage-Turner syndrome
Pemphigus vulgaris
Pernicious anaemia
POEMS syndrome
Polyarteritis nodosa
Polymyalgia rheumatica
Polymyositis
Postmyocardial infarction syndrome
Postpericardiotomy syndrome
Primary biliary cirrhosis
Primary sclerosing cholangitis
Psoriasis
Psoriatic arthritis
Pure red cell aplasia
Pyoderma gangrenosum
Raynaud's phenomenon
Reactive arthritis
Relapsing polychondritis
Restless leg syndrome
Retroperitoneal fibrosis
Rheumatic fever
Rheumatoid arthritis
Sarcoidosis
Scleroderma
Sjogren's syndrome
Stiff person syndrome
Subacute bacterial endocarditis
Susac's syndrome
Sympathetic ophthalmia
Systemic lupus erythematosus
Tolosa-Hunt syndrome
Transverse myelitis
Ulcerative colitis
Undifferentiated connective tissue disease
Vasculitis
Vitiligo

In colitis, the antibody response results in the body attacking the gut. It causes swelling and ulcers to form on the gut surface which bleed and produce pus. These ulcers can weaken the gut wall and cause further 'holes,' which allow bacteria to enter the bloodstream.

So, how do we stop this process once it has started? Well, we have to remove the trigger to the whole process. For this, the solution is to remove gluten to stop further zonulin production and to address any bacterial imbalances in the gut. Then healing the gut is crucial to close up those tight junctions by restoring their integrity. When the tight junctions start to work correctly again, glucose, amino acids and fatty acids are forced to pass through the cells as normal and therefore the immune system is no longer stimulated. This allows the immune response to gradually decrease, the body stops producing antibodies and, therefore, there are slowly fewer antibodies available to attack the body. With less and less exposure to gluten, and a restoration of proper bacterial levels, the gut barrier restores to normal. Hence, the antibody level eventually subsides to almost none and so the autoimmune condition begins to settle.

This is where conventional medicine falls short. Medication will settle the inflammation, but nothing is done to help heal the gut and restore tight junction integrity or to remove the root cause of the problem. It is assumed that healing will happen all on its own without providing additional nutrients to help the body repair itself. Hence, when a flare settles, it is only a matter of time before the gut is damaged again, as the root cause has not been addressed and the tight junctions are still open or 'leaky'.

top tip

Eat the colours of the rainbow: Different coloured fruit and vegetables give you different vitamins and minerals, so eating a good range of colours ensures you get them all

healing the gut

We can change our diets until they are the best in the world but unless we address issues in the gut it will not do much good. We have to ensure our guts are the most efficient that they can be at breaking down our food and absorbing it through the gut wall. Eating the right foods will ensure a good supply of the vitamins and minerals that we need to make stomach acid and digestive enzymes, but how can we heal a damaged gut wall and replenish good bacteria?

Nutritional therapy aims to tackle the root cause of conditions. It looks at the whole person and not just at individual parts. Our body parts interact and when we have a problem with one area it impacts on another. By reviewing every system in the body and piecing together a person's symptoms, a full picture is gained of the effects of any condition on the entire body. As a nutritional therapist I often talk to my clients about the "5 R principle of gut healing", as outlined by The Institute for Functional Medicine (see references at the end of the first section). The first part of the programme is to:

REMOVE any foods to which you are intolerant from your diet. This can be a very difficult thing to establish because, if you have developed a 'leaky gut', you probably react to multiple foods and so a clear picture is almost impossible to obtain. You have two options, either:

- Remove the biggest culprits – gluten and dairy – for one month and see how this alters your symptoms; or

- See a nutritional therapist who will help you to find out what is most likely to be irritating your gut - there are various additional symptoms which can point a therapist in the direction of one cause or another.

Dairy is extremely difficult for the body to digest due to the large size of the protein in it, casein, and often causes problems in those individuals susceptible to digestive issues.

Having removed the foods you react to, you also need to think about removing any possible parasites, bacteria or yeast that may be resident in the gut. Bacteria and yeast are easier to remove as you can eat foods that will help to kill them off naturally. This includes foods like:

- Garlic – particularly raw as it kills off bacteria (see the recipe for olive tapenade);

- Oregano – it is a natural antibiotic, include it in its dry form or add a little oil to food. Be careful though, this is more potent and should only be used short-term as it can kill off good bacteria too; and

- Coconut oil – it is highly anti-fungal so will help with any yeast infection or overgrowth. Roast vegetables in it, use it to fry-off food or add it to smoothies.

If you suspect a parasite then go and see your GP, especially if you have passed a worm in your stool, as this requires proper testing and treatment.

After removing the offending foods, you next need to REPLACE any missing components that are needed for good digestion to occur. These include the vitamins and minerals needed by your body to make sufficient quantities of digestive enzymes, bile and stomach acid. If you have undigested food in your stool, other than sweetcorn, then you are not digesting very well. You may need to add a digestive enzyme to your daily regime temporarily, while you work on increasing your vitamin and mineral intake, which will enable your body to make more of your own. You may also need to take a probiotic, as good bacteria produce digestive enzymes too and you may be a little low in these. Or you can eat fermented foods that contain natural bacteria in them. Make sure that any bought versions are unpasteurised as the pasteurisation process will kill off any bacteria present. Examples of good foods containing probiotics are sauerkraut, kefir, miso and kimchi. Choose the water kefir so that you avoid a milk based one.

Your stool should be a mid-brown colour. If it is green (after eating lots of spinach / kale) or purple (after eating beetroot) then it is a sign that these foods are not being broken down properly. This further substantiates your need for a digestive enzyme and probiotics. Be careful with supplementing a digestive enzyme if you have Crohn's or Colitis or any form of Gastritis as they can irritate the gut. Please check with the supplement company before you buy one whether they are suitable. We didn't use one with Richard just to be sure we wouldn't do any harm.

Bile is released from the gall bladder into the gut via the bile duct and helps us to break down fat in our diet. The liver makes bile out of cholesterol. If bile acid levels are high, our body makes less cholesterol, if they are low it makes more cholesterol. Therefore, if cholesterol levels are high in your body it suggests you have low bile acid levels. You therefore need to boost bile flow to reduce cholesterol levels. To boost your bile flow, eat bitter foods like radish, artichoke, rocket and endive. Herbal teas containing dandelion also help. If you have problems digesting greasy food or indigestion after eating fat, this may indicate that bile is a little low. I find the easiest way to incorporate bitter foods is to have a rocket and radish side salad to accompany a meal.

If your stomach acid is low you can develop acne rosacea (red nose and cheeks which flush easily). You can also get indigestion trying to eat large portions of meat. Many people may actually have no idea that low stomach acid is a problem. Acid reflux can also be a sign that your levels of stomach acid are low. This may sound bizarre, but carbohydrate digestion starts in the mouth and should stop in the stomach, if there is sufficient acid. High quantities of acid result in the pH value being low. The pH value needs to be low for optimal protein digestion and this also stops amylase from breaking down carbohydrates. However, if you do not produce enough acid the pH value is too high for protein digestion but continues to be sufficient for carbohydrates to be digested. This produces gas which pushes back on the valve that closes off your stomach to your food pipe from the throat (oesophagus). This allows stomach acid to flow back up the pipe and give you that burning feeling. Ironically, GPs usually prescribe acid suppressants (like omeprazole) to prevent this reflux, when in actual fact we should be raising acid levels to prevent it.

It is possible to buy supplements that contain stomach acid, should you wish to raise levels, but you need to be really careful with them. If you have any form of gastritis or a previous stomach ulcer, do not touch them. In fact, I would advise that you only take them under the supervision of a therapist because, taking them incorrectly can cause a stomach ulcer. They are also inadvisable if you have Crohn's or colitis. You can also get some products that are a combination of stomach acid and digestive enzymes, these work really well as they tick both boxes. Or, you could try good old apple cider vinegar before meals (1 tablespoon in a small glass of water) but again, do not do this if you have any history of ulcers. If you are taking any medication that lowers stomach acid do not take any apple cider vinegar, as it will counteract its affects.

Next you need to eat to help REPAIR the gut....

- Glutamine is an amino acid that the gut uses as fuel. It can be found in cabbage so, you have guessed it, you need to increase the amount of cabbage that you eat. It can be enjoyed as:

  - sauerkraut – make your own or buy it in but make sure it is not pasteurised because it will then also provide good bacteria - see later recipe on page ????;

  - put it in soup;

  - put it in a juice; or

  - steam it and then fry it off with a little coconut oil to improve the taste.

Cabbage juice is a great healer, research actually shows that it can heal stomach ulcers. We had a lot of cabbage in smoothies and made sauerkraut.

- Butyrate is another fuel needed by the gut, and is made by good bacteria converting any insoluble fibre that you eat. Low butyrate levels have been linked to an increased risk of colon cancer. Good sources of insoluble fibre include bananas, sweet potatoes, turnip, artichoke hearts, carrots or beetroot. Have a look on page 59 for a great little recipe for a side dish which you can make containing a variety of these;

- Pectin can be found in the skin of apples. It is great because again, it feeds beneficial bacteria but has the added benefit of providing bulk to the stools, thereby helping to 'cleanse' the colon and restore the integrity of tight junctions. See the stewed apple recipe on page 59. You need to eat at least 2-3 portions of this a week to be effective; and

- Chicken bone broth not only provides glutamine, but also collagen and glucosamine which are good for joints. See the recipe later on page 60 for the best way to make the broth. If you have any kind of joint issue then this is a regular must do. Crucially, it also contains gelatin which helps to improve tight junction integrity. Make sure you use an organic chicken so that you avoid any toxin exposure.

REINOCULATE follows repairing the gut...

Next you need to eat fermented vegetables to replenish beneficial bacteria. Examples include sauerkraut (p58), kimchi or fermented beets. You should eat these two to three times a week if possible. You can also consume kefir as a source of good bacteria.

If you do not like the sound of any fermented vegetables or kefir, then you need to take a probiotic to replace the good bacteria. Now, not all probiotics are produced equally, and by that I mean, if they are cheap, they probably will not make it through the stomach acid to reach the gut alive. You will be much better spending a little more and getting a clinically proven product in order to ensure that it does what it says it will. Some brands contain bacteria in too low numbers to be of benefit, if you are trying to reinoculate. Get one with at least 10-15 billion per capsule.

Whilst reinoculating we also need to ensure that we are feeding the beneficial bacteria that we are putting into the gut. They feed on fibre found in sweet potato, turnip, carrots, beetroot and artichoke. It is also worth bearing in mind here, that removing the food source for harmful bacteria will help to bring your gut back into balance more quickly. Reduce considerably, or stop entirely for now, your intake of processed food, white potatoes, parsnips or white rice.

Finally you need to REBALANCE. Life isn't just about eating. See the next chapter for further advice on lifestyle changes beneficial to healing.

If you are doing all of this on your own you also need to be careful. If you have any of the following symptoms, that your GP is unaware of, you must get them checked out as they can have serious causes:

- Blood in your stools;

- Mucus in your stools;

- Black poo (if you are not on iron tablets or taking charcoal);

- Something resembling dried coffee grounds in your stool;

- Constant abdominal pain;

- Changes to your normal bowel habits – either severe constipation or diarrhoea; or

- Clay coloured stools.

top tip

Dried beans or chickpeas need to be soaked for at least twelve hours, drained, rinsed and cooked with fresh water to remove toxins!

lifestyle chapter

In order to achieve our optimum health we also need to balance our work and relaxation times. We need to sleep soundly and for long enough, exercise regularly, be mindful and hydrate ourselves sufficiently. It is not enough today to just change your diet, you need to look at everything that is impacting on you and your environment as these will all add to, or subtract from, your overall health.

So let us have a look at some of the other factors that we need to take into consideration when trying to heal ourselves.

work

Work can be very stressful. Stress in itself depletes vital nutrients from our bodies, because the adrenal system works to respond to the stress in order to cope with the situation. Either we need to look at decreasing stress or, if that's not possible, we need to be able to cope better by balancing our blood sugar and eating nutrients to support the adrenal system.

Ways to help reduce our stress at work include:

- Take regular breaks – this does not have to mean leaving work, it can be walking to the photocopier, getting a drink of water, walking to talk to a colleague instead of using the phone. Go for a walk at lunch to help clear your mind. Try listening to music or go and sit in your car and do 10 mins deep breathing exercises / meditation to calm you down;

- Re-structuring the day – if you find particular areas of your workload more stressful than others, and you have control of your day, then schedule these for just before lunch or at the end of the day when you are about to relax straight after. Or, if something is bothering you, get that task done straight away so that you can move on; and

- Delegate more – if you have too much to do and not enough time, then delegate more or ask for help. We all need to realise that we have limitations, we are not super beings with special powers to achieve everything all at the same time. Acknowledging what you cannot get done on your own is not a weakness.

The other really important thing about being at work is NOT to continue to work through your lunch. There is a phrase 'rest and digest'. You're not going to do this if you are still sat at your desk continuing with paperwork whilst you eat. Stress shuts down digestion, so leave your desk and have a change of scenery, to switch off from your work and to bring down your stress levels before you try to eat. Research shows that the stress hormone cortisol actually causes the blood supply to your gut to divert to your muscles to prepare you to run away from the stress, hence you get indigestion as you simply can't break down your food.

If your source of stress is family or friends then please take steps to try and resolve this:

- Try talking it over and resolving the disagreement;

- Exercise to clear your mind – this does not have to be pounding a treadmill at the gym, it can be walking the dog. Make it a regular part of your day and stick to it;

- Take time for yourself each day – have a hot bath, read a book, meditate or take up a hobby; or

- Try an Epsom salt foot bath – Epsom salts contain magnesium which is a very calming mineral that helps you to relax. Try it 30 minutes before bed as it helps your brain to switch off before sleep. Keep your feet in for 20 minutes and then dab dry so that you don't remove all of the salts.

When you simply cannot remove stress and you just have to get through it, then you need to take measures to support your adrenal system to avoid burnout. The adrenal system needs protein, magnesium and B vitamins to function effectively, so get eating brown rice, lentils, green leafy vegetables, nuts and seeds. In order to cope with stress you also need to balance your blood sugar well. Balancing your blood sugar can be difficult but, by following some basic rules, you can make a real difference to how you can cope with life in general. These rules include:

- Never skip meals, which avoids low sugar situations;

- Eat protein with every meal and snack, as this delays the emptying of the stomach and, hence, you get a more even energy release. Protein is found in meat, fish, eggs, lentils, beans, quinoa, nuts or seeds;

- Eat low sugar fruits on their own (berries, kiwi, oranges, pears, apples), but high sugar fruits (banana, mango, grapes and melon) must be eaten with a handful of nuts to prevent spiking your blood sugar;

- Eliminate fizzy drinks, cakes, biscuits, fruit juices, again to prevent spiking your blood sugar;

- Eat whole foods – brown rice, vegetables, meat, nuts, fish and seeds, as these contain a good mix of nutrients and fibre, which also reduce sugar spikes;

- Avoid stimulants such as caffeine and alcohol as they stimulate the adrenals; and

- Don't eat low fat foods as they are high in sugar - that's how they get the taste - but they will spike your blood sugar if eaten on their own. If you want to avoid this but still eat them, add seeds to yogurt to get the protein combination and prevent the sugar surge.

sleep

A good night's sleep is more important than you might think. We need to be getting between 7-8 hours of sleep a night to get adequate rest for our bodies to cope with the day's activity. Whilst we sleep, our bodies are performing all of the 'housekeeping' that we need to do to ensure good health. During the day our body is preoccupied with eating, breaking down and using nutrients from our food and producing energy for any movement. It is only when we effectively fast during the night that our bodies have time to clear away dead cells, repair areas of damage, filter the blood and remove toxins from the body. If we do not achieve good, deep sleep, the body has less time to perform its necessary jobs and our system simply does not function as effectively. If you have problems sleeping you need to:

- Go to bed at the same time each night – get into a pattern – our bodies respond well to regular patterns;

- Get up at the same time;

- Have a completely dark room to avoid light making the brain think that it is morning;

- Remove all electronics or loud ticking clocks that may disturb your sleep; and

- Ensure you are getting plenty of magnesium. It is a very calming mineral which stops an overactive brain, but it also relaxes muscles and so helps us to settle down and drift off to sleep. You can try Epsom salt baths as mentioned before or increase your intake of green leafy vegetables, nuts and seeds to get it from a dietary source.

exercise

We all know exercise is good for us, as it:

- prevents muscle degradation;

- builds new muscle;

- stimulates the release of endorphins which are natural painkillers;

- helps us to maintain weight;

- prevents osteoporosis;

- improves blood flow; and

- improves insulin sensitivity.

Ideally, we need to move every day for at least 30 minutes if we can. Do whatever you can within pain limits. This does not mean you have to run every day, it just means move however you can. A good brisk walk will do, ideally such that you can just maintain a conversation. Or you can try swimming, cycling or going to the gym. Find something that works for you, get into a routine and stick to it. If it is too hard or you do not enjoy it, you will stop eventually. So, choose wisely.

And for everyone over the age of 40, resistance exercise is crucial to prevent losing muscle mass. This does not have to be weights at the gym. It can just be body resisted exercises like the plank, wall sit, chair dips, squats or lunges at home.

It is also worth mentioning here, that a walk outside in the sun will boost your Vitamin D levels. It is known to regulate inflammation and helps to balance the immune system. 10-15 minutes a day is sufficient, without cream on. However, if you live in Scotland like we do, I would recommend supplementing from the end of October until the end of March as the sun just isn't strong enough to boost our levels and we don't see it often enough! Again, check with a professional before you take it if you are on medication. If you have the autoimmune condition sarcoidosis Vitamin D supplementation is contraindicated.

mindfulness

We are becoming more and more aware of mindfulness. Even my 12 year old son has had lessons in mindfulness recently. Some people swear by it, others are more sceptical. I would say the main thing is just listening to your body more. We are very good at ignoring the warning signs and glossing over minor symptoms because we do not have time for whatever reason. Mindfulness teaches us to slow down, be more aware of our surroundings and to listen to our bodies. Some people take time out every day to do deep breathing techniques and really feel how their bodies are. Some people just take time to pause after a meal. Whatever works for you to get more aware of your body is fine. If you are tired, rest. If you eat something and get indigestion, find out whether it was the food or the environment in which you ate it that caused the problem. If you are stressed or rushing, your digestion is literally shut down, as your body diverts blood away from your stomach to use in the muscles to 'run away' from the situation (the 'fight or flight' reaction). If you think there is a reason for a symptom remove it and see how you feel.

hydration

Our bodies are 60% water, so it is no surprise that we need to make sure that we replenish it often. Water is needed:

- for our cells to work properly;
- for us to maintain regular bowel movements;
- to maintain our temperature - through the sweating mechanism; and
- for our kidneys to filter well.

Don't forget, only water and herbal teas count towards your 6-8 glasses per day that you need to get. Coffee, tea and alcohol detract from your total and some herbal teas may have diuretics in them too, so watch out for them.

*   *   *   *   *

You need to do the whole 5R programme (remove, replace, repair, reinoculate, rebalance) for at least three months to allow time for any antibody reaction to subside. After these three months you can think about trying to reintroduce any foods that you have removed, if your symptoms have fully settled.

If you have an autoimmune disease, you will probably need to leave them out for much longer in order to let symptoms clear. For Richard, we left gluten and dairy out for about 9 months before trying them again. For him, gluten was and still is the main issue, so he only has it very infrequently, but he was able to bring back in all goat's dairy and occasional cow's dairy*. The main thing is that you need to listen to your own body and see what works for you.

*The protein, casein, in goat's dairy is in a different form to that in cow's milk and is much easier to digest so people can often tolerate it.

food reintroduction

When reintroducing foods you only choose one at a time. If more than one is introduced at the same time and adverse reactions are seen you cannot determine which of the foods caused them. You then have to remove them all for 3 weeks again before you can reintroduce them. Therefore, choose your food and eat it 2 – 3 times in one day and record any symptoms in the chart below for up to 48 hours after you ate the food. Do not test a second food until after the 48 hours has finished. It is possible to get a delayed reaction to a particular food so this ensures you have successfully tested it.

Date	Time	Food	Digestion / Bowel Function	Joint / Muscle aches	Headache	Nasal congestion	Skin reaction	Energy Levels

If you get a reaction to a food, you need to remove it again from your diet for a further three months to allow the antibody reaction to fully settle before trying again. Or it may be that you need to leave it out completely. Some people find that once they have settled their response they can eat the food on a rotational basis (once every four days) and not flare any symptoms. Everyone is different, you just need to experiment and find out what works for you.

top tip

A word on gut bacteria.....
They perform a major role in our immune systems, make vitamins and breakdown fibre to help fight against cancer. Feed the good, starve the bad and boost their numbers.

removing the right food

If you have IBS or general feelings of digestive discomfort after certain foods, the best place to start is to remove gluten due to its known effect on gut integrity. If you have a direct correlation between a type of food and your symptoms, take out those foods too. This is where you really need to listen to what your body is telling you. It will be giving you clues but we are normally so busy that we do not pay attention. As a general rule, if gluten is a problem it tends to cause digestive issues with painful joints, swelling and stiffness. Dairy tends to cause digestive issues with sinusitis, excess nasal mucus and dry skin. Watch out though, as gluten intolerance can also cause psoriasis (as this is an autoimmune condition), so you could have a rather clouded picture. Be aware that you could exhibit any of the food intolerance signs (shown in the table below) with any of the intolerances. My advice would be to go with gluten- and dairy-free first, clean up your diet and then see what symptoms you are left with.

If you already have an autoimmune disease (see list on page 25 & 26) you need to go straight in with being gluten- and dairy-free. They are by far the two most likely food intolerances for individuals with an established autoimmune disease. In this situation, it is most likely that you will need to find out what you are intolerant to and keep it out of your diet long term. You can still probably have a little now and then once you have settled your condition, but a full return to eating it is likely to restart your problem. It is extremely important here that you do work to heal the gut, removing the irritation is the start, but you must work to heal yourself too.

Symptoms of a possible food intolerance include:

Fatigue, brain fog, poor concentration, hyperactivity, restlessness	Binge eating/drinking, food cravings
Headaches, migraines, insomnia, dizziness	Runny nose, post nasal drip, watery/itchy eyes, ear infections, excessive mucus, dark circles under eyes, tinnitus, swollen eyelids
Joint aches/pain, arthritis, swelling and stiffness	Nausea, vomiting
Frequently clearing throat, coughing, hoarseness, sore gums	Constipation, diarrhoea, IBS, indigestion, bloating, flatulence, cramps, heartburn
Anxiety, mood swings, irritability, aggression, depression	Irregular heartbeat, asthma, bronchitis
Skin problems - rashes, hives, dry skin, acne, psoriasis, eczema	Weight issues – over or underweight

Fluid retention, frequent urination, bed-wetting	Children can also have: • ADHD • Behaviour issues • Learning problems • Recurring ear infections
Hair loss	Excessive sweating

As you can see there are lots of other symptoms, that you would not guess are linked to a possible food intolerance and some even that you would ignore as something minor, but they all can be part of the same problem. If you think you may have Coeliac disease do not remove any gluten until you have seen your GP. Go and get yourself tested with the blood test. Do NOT remove gluten from your diet, because in order for them to do the test, they will tell you that you have to be eating gluten 6 times a day for 6 weeks to ensure that the test gives you a proper result (that is what our GP told us anyway). If you remove gluten and your symptoms improve and then you go to your GP, they will ask you to restart eating gluten to do the test. That means enduring your symptoms again just to get the test done. So, see your GP first and if you get a negative result you have 2 options. The first one being to go it alone and remove the above foods from your diet and see how you get on or go to see a nutritional therapist for help.

If you decide to go it alone, then you must remove all sources of gluten for it to be a success. It will not work if your remove most of it, you will still get the antibody reaction even if you eat one crumb of it so it is an all-or-nothing scenario.

See the tables below for what you find gluten and dairy in and what the alternatives are.

Foods containing gluten:

Batter	Beer
Biscuits	Bread inc. bagels / croissants / croutons / crackers / crumpets / naan / tortillas
Breadcrumbs	Breakfast cereals
Cakes	Couscous
Crisps – check label, some are allowed	Flour
Ice cream (wheat)	Ketchup
Mustard	Pasta inc. ravioli / noodles
Pastry	Pizza bases
Pork Pie	Ready meals
Sauces – pre made and includes soy sauce	Sausages - hot dogs
Soups – tinned	Stock cubes

Sweets	Food additives, such as malt flavouring, modified food starch, MSG and others
Medications and vitamins that use gluten as a binding agent	

(Please note – research now suggests that whisky, vodka and gin do NOT contain gluten as they have had it removed by distillation. This is not the case for beer.)

Gluten-free grains include: brown rice, buckwheat, amaranth, millet, oats, quinoa and sorghum. Watch out for possible cross contamination with oats so buy the gluten-free ones to ensure they are actually gluten free.

Foods containing dairy:

Milk – cows, goats and sheep	Yogurt
Cheese	Cream
Ice cream	Crème fraiche
Chocolate	Butter
Fromage frais	Biscuits / cakes
Buttermilk	Some breakfast cereals
Cottage cheese	Dips / sauces
Whey	Some desserts
Quark	

Dairy alternatives include:

Nut milks – almond / coconut	Hemp milk
Nutritional yeast	Soya milk
Soya yogurt or cheese	Pura spread – alternate to butter
Oat milk	Nut butters – almond or cashew
Dark chocolate (85%)	Rice milk
Coconut oil	Dairy-free ice cream
Tofu	Soya desserts

Caution: Only have one portion of soya a day. It is highly processed and can be another major food intolerance. Also, watch out, dairy-free ice cream will normally contain gluten used as a thickener.

Obviously, if you take dairy out of your diet, you have to ensure that you get enough calcium to maintain good bone health. Listed below are foods that are high in calcium that you can eat to replace what you do not get from dairy. In fact, the calcium in these foods is more easily available to the body than that in dairy so, as long as you get them into your diet regularly, your calcium levels should remain sufficiently high. Please do ask your GP to test if you are concerned about your calcium intake, particularly if you are a post-menopausal woman.

Broccoli / sprouts	Sesame / pumpkin / sunflower seeds
Fish with bones eg. tinned salmon / mackerel / sardines	Tahini
Parsley	Green leafy vegetables – spinach / kale
Almond milk	Almonds

There are lots of gluten- and dairy-free alternatives in the 'free from' sections of the supermarkets, so it is far easier now than it was ten years ago when we first started. However, I would recommend if you are trying to recover from an autoimmune disease or any other serious problem, that you leave out all processed food to give you maximum chance of recovery. Processed food is full of additives and preservatives so is best omitted, if you want to optimise your health.

I do appreciate, however, that the desire for bread may get strong. We have found the best alternatives are M&S Sourdough, Warburtons thins or Bfree sweet potato wraps. Of course it really is not like real bread, but it should just settle the craving without blowing your diet. Gluten-free pasta tastes the same as normal pasta, but does turn the water a bit milky. Do not worry as you are tipping it away anyway! It can get stuck together, so stir it a bit more often than normal.

Do not forget gluten and dairy are the main two food intolerances, but you can also react to soy, nightshade vegetables (white potato, tomatoes, bell peppers, aubergine) egg, corn and pork, so you may need to check some of these possibilities out too.

diet basics

So, after all this talk of food, what are we going to be eating? Let's have a look at the basics, so we all know exactly what we are talking about, and then we will put it all together.

proteins

What are they?

Foods that contain proteins are broken down into amino acids. We cannot absorb proteins when they are large but we can when they are split into their smaller units.

What are they needed for?

We cannot survive without protein. It is needed for numerous processes within the body:

- to build and repair body tissue – muscles, collagen, ligaments, tendons, etc.;
- to help transport the things we need in the body;
- to speed up chemical reactions – with enzymes;
- to help us move – our muscles; and
- to defend our bodies against bacteria and viruses – our antibodies.

What can we find them in?

All meat, fish, dairy, beans, lentils, quinoa, eggs, nuts and seeds. Not all protein is the healthiest for you though. The best forms to eat more of are grass-fed beef or lamb, organic chicken, fish, eggs, quinoa, nuts and seeds.

We need to be a little careful of what fish we eat as some of them contain mercury. I have included a list below of fish to eat and those to avoid due to their high mercury content. Try as much as possible to choose wild-caught fresh fish.

Fish and seafood typically with **LOW** mercury levels:

Anchovy	Pacific cod	Haddock
Wild salmon	Scallops	Shrimps
Herring	Sole	Perch
Hake	Trout	

Fish and seafood typically with **HIGH** mercury levels:

Tuna	Other Cod	Shark
Farmed salmon	Swordfish	Oysters
Crab	Sea bass	

Wild salmon, sardines and mackerel are particularly good for you as sources of omega 3 fats, which are essential for good functioning of all the cells in your body. They are also extremely anti-inflammatory so excellent to include in any diet where inflammation is an issue.

If you eat beans and lentils, make sure you prepare them properly, as they can be very difficult for the body to digest. They contain phytates and saponins that prevent their breakdown. They can also bind to other beneficial nutrients in your gut and remove them from your body. If you soak the dry ones overnight before use, this can remove some of the phytates/saponins and therefore reduce their effect. I would suggest that anyone who is suffering with health issues should avoid these completely initially. They can reintroduce them when their symptoms have settled down, as they do provide a good range of nutrients when prepared properly.

carbohydrates

What are they?

Carbohydrates can be classed as either simple (sugars) or complex (starch). Simple carbohydrates are those which are broken down very quickly into sugar. Complex carbohydrates are sugar in very long chains so take much longer to break down and, therefore, do not spike your blood sugar quite as high as quickly. However, they still do cause a significant rise in blood sugar compared to protein and fats.

What are they needed for?

Carbohydrates are used for energy. They are quickly broken down into glucose and used to fuel all cells in the body. A good supply helps you exercise, run your metabolism and fuel your brain.

However, it could be argued that we eat them in excessive quantities nowadays. Our lives are much more sedentary than our ancestors and, therefore, our energy requirements are much lower. Yet, we don't seem to compensate for this by reducing our carbohydrate intake accordingly, perhaps one of the reasons that obesity is becoming such an issue.

What can we find them in?

Simple carbohydrates include sugar, honey and sweet fruits, whilst complex carbs include things like bread, pasta and rice.

fats

Fats get a lot of bad press but they are absolutely essential for life. Vitamins A, D, E and K can only be absorbed, if you eat them with a meal that contains fat. Also, many hormones are made from cholesterol and cannot be synthesised without it.

What are they?

Fats are normally split into saturated fats, monounsaturated fats and polyunsaturated fats. All fats are similar in chemical structure and consist of a chain of carbon atoms bonded to hydrogen atoms. Where they differ is the length of the carbon chain and the number of hydrogen atoms that they bond to. These differences lead to them being in different forms and affect their function in the body. For example, saturated fats are solid at room temperature, because the chain of carbon atoms has as many hydrogen atoms as possible. Monounsaturated fats are liquid at room temperature due to a carbon to carbon double bond that results in two fewer hydrogen atoms. Polyunsaturated fats have two or more carbon double bonds so have even fewer hydrogen atoms, they are typically liquid at room temperature too.

Saturated fats tend to be the more unhealthy fats as they can raise cholesterol levels in the body, with the exception being coconut oil which is used directly for energy. Polyunsaturated and monounsaturated fats are considered healthy, especially polyunsaturated fats. Omega 3 is a type of polyunsaturated fat. They are considered essential because they are needed for good body function and you cannot make them yourself.

Fats are broken down into fatty acids and glycerol before they are used in the body.

What are they needed for?

Our cells all have an outer cell wall that is made up of fat, which controls what comes into a cell, what goes out and any signals that pass between cells. It also forms the basis of all inflammatory responses. When a cell is injured, fats are released from the cell wall in order to make substances that regulate the inflammatory response. Depending on what fats are in the cell wall, our bodies produce substances that promote more inflammation or help to calm it. Hence, we can eat an anti-inflammatory diet because, if we include more healthy fats in our diet, we can influence our inflammatory response. Don't forget inflammation is a normal part of healing, but it should occur when required and then stop. It is just when inflammation doesn't stop and becomes chronic that we need to do something about it.

Fat is also used structurally, to transport things in the body and is the building block for some hormones and bile (needed for digestion).

What can we find them in?

Good fats include coconut oil, olive oil, flax oil, avocados, nuts and seeds. Bad fats include vegetable oils, fried food, cakes, pastries, biscuits, sugar-filled food and saturated animal fat.

fruit & vegetables

The World Health Organisation (WHO) says that we need around 10 portions of fruit and vegetables per day to ensure we get enough fibre and nutrients for health. This is for two reasons. Firstly, our soil today does not contain the same level of nutrients as it did years ago, so our fruit and vegetables don't contain the same levels of nutrients either. Secondly, we are exposed to far more toxins in our daily lives than we previously were, so need more antioxidants to counteract them. Trying to get 10 portions in a day is not as difficult as you think. A pint of smoothie for breakfast, a bowl of soup or a salad count as 3 portions. The UK Government (Chief Medical Officer) advice chose five a day because they thought it was easier to achieve. Easier, yes, but not good for optimum health. If you think you are consistently falling short of this you could consider taking a good multivitamin.

You also need to think variety. Choose a wide range of colours to ensure you get all of the vitamins and minerals that you need, think colours of the rainbow. I have included a list below to remind you of a few fruit and vegetables that you may have forgotten.

Red:

Fruit	Vegetables
Red apples	Beetroot
Cherries	Red peppers
Cranberries	Radishes
Red grapes	Red onions
Red grapefruit	Rhubarb
Raspberries / strawberries	Tomatoes
Watermelon	

Yellow/orange:

Fruit	Vegetables
Apricots	Butternut squash
Cantaloupe	Carrots
Grapefruit	Yellow peppers
Lemons	Pumpkin
Mangoes	Sweet potatoes
Nectarines	Yellow tomatoes
Oranges / satsumas / tangerines	
Peaches	
Pineapple	

White or brown:

Fruit	Vegetables
Bananas	Cauliflower
Dates	Garlic
	Ginger
	Jerusalem artichoke
	Mushrooms
	Onions
	Shallots
	Turnips

Green:

Fruit	Vegetables
Avocados	Artichokes
Green apples	Rocket
Green grapes	Asparagus
Honeydew melon	Broccoli
Kiwi	Brussel sprouts
Limes	Cabbage
	Green beans
	Celery
	Cucumbers
	Peas
	Leeks
	Lettuce
	Spinach
	Watercress
	Sugar snap peas
	Mange tout
	Green peppers
	Courgette
	Kale
	Olives

Blue / purple:

Fruit	Vegetables
Blackberries	Black olives
Blueberries	Purple asparagus
Blackcurrants	Purple cabbage
Plums	Aubergine
Elderberries	Purple endive
Purple grapes	
Raisins	
Figs	

putting it all together – what to eat

So, putting all of these previous chapters into action what did we do? Essentially, we ate a wholefood, unprocessed diet. We removed dairy, gluten and all other processed food eating only fresh fruit, vegetables, meat, fish, nuts and seeds. It is essentially eating a Paleo diet but with the emphasis on certain foods to help heal the gut. I have listed it all in the tables below to make it easy. We tried to eat local, seasonal foods to reduce any toxic load on our systems and ensure variety.

food to eat:

Poultry – chicken or turkey	Eggs	Quinoa
Venison	Fish – esp. salmon, mackerel, sardines	Starchy vegetables – sweet potato, carrots, turnips, butternut squash
Beef – once per week	Nuts – esp. almonds, walnuts, brazil	Seeds – sesame, pumpkin & sunflower
Lamb – once per week	Smoothies	Juices – freshly prepared – vegetable-based best
Avocado	Cook with coconut oil / olive oil on salads	Fermented foods – sauerkraut, kefir
Herbs & spices esp. turmeric, ginger, garlic, cinnamon, cayenne	Coconut milk, unsweetened almond milk, soya milk	Leafy green vegetables – broccoli, spinach, kale, bok choy, lettuce, rocket, cabbage
Rainbow coloured veg – tomatoes, peppers, leeks, mushrooms	Fruit – esp. low sugar – berries, oranges, kiwi, apples, pears, plums	Brown rice, gluten-free oats
Cruciferous veg – sprouts, cauliflower	Coffee / tea with meals only. We had no coffee to begin with	Water

food to avoid:

Gluten	Sugar	Beans / lentils (initially)	Dairy
Minimal smoked meats / fish	All processed food	Minimal white potatoes	Fruit juices
Fizzy drinks	Artificial sweeteners – use honey or stevia if needed	Low fat foods – they are high in sugar	

On the following pages are some sample menus to help you get the idea of what food we ate.

top tip

Did you know?
You have to eat fat to be able to absorb vitamins A, D, E and K. So get some olive oil on your salad to absorb your vitamins from your veggies

6 day menu

day one

Breakfast - Smoothie – 1 handful oats, almond milk or water (1 glassful), frozen berries – handful blueberries and raspberries, 1 heaped dessert spoon ground almonds and 1 tablespoon ground linseeds and a banana – blend

Lunch - Salad – spinach, watercress and rocket mixed leaves, handful mixed seeds (sesame, sunflower and pumpkin), spring onion, cucumber, tomato. Add to this either mackerel/sardines/chicken/boiled egg/avocado. Dressing – drizzle over olive oil and balsamic vinegar. Have with a spoonful of sauerkraut and a spoon of probiotic side dish.

Snack (3.30/4.00) – Kiwi (if needed)

Dinner – Steamed, grilled or oven-baked fish with steamed vegetables and sweet potato fries. Have a little olive tapenade on the side.

day two

Breakfast – Homemade muesli – oats, sunflower/pumpkin seeds, raisins or cranberries, blueberries with almond milk or coconut milk blended with frozen berries

Lunch – Quinoa salad – peas, cucumber, avocado, chicken, tomato, mushrooms – whatever you fancy (see recipe later). Cold salmon, spring onion etc. Have with a spoonful of sauerkraut and rocket and radish side salad.

Snack (3.30/4.00) – Pear (if needed)

Dinner – Homemade fishcakes – white fish combined with spring onion, herbs and mashed sweet potato – serve with vegetables or salad. Have stewed apple and cinnamon for dessert.

day three

Breakfast – Fruit salad (mango, strawberries, apple) with coconut milk & frozen berry yogurt and one tablespoon of ground linseeds

Lunch – Soup – tomato & basil with quinoa, carrot & coriander with quinoa, lentil with 2/3 gluten-free oatcakes. Make soup with chicken bone broth.

Snack (3.30/4.00) – Blueberries with 3-4 brazil nuts (if needed)

Dinner – Chicken stir fry with lots of vegetables (mangetout, carrot, peppers) – add a little water with the oil to try to steam fry – serve with rice noodles or courgetti (courgettes spiralised or grated into strips). Experiment with herbs to garnish and spices (Chinese five spice works well).

day four

Breakfast – Porridge made with almond milk and with one dessert spoon ground almonds mixed in. Top with blueberries and linseeds or put stewed apple and cinnamon on top.

Lunch – Spring onion, mushrooms and cherry tomatoes heated in a pan with garlic and paprika served on gluten-free toast with avocado cubed and placed on top. Accompany with a rocket and radish side salad.

Snack (3.30/4.00) – Satsuma (if needed)

Dinner – Grilled chicken with beetroot relish, broccoli and roasted butternut squash fries. Have with a little olive tapenade and probiotic side dish.

day five

Breakfast – Juice – 1 apple, 1 small beetroot, 1 carrot, ½ lemon with rind on, 1 inch cucumber, 1 stick celery, 2 large slices off ½ a cabbage (to help fuel gut cells) plus after juicing blend in half an avocado

Lunch – Brown rice salad – peas, cucumber, salmon, spring onion, tomato, rocket, mixed seeds with a little sauerkraut on the side

Snack – (3.30/4.00) Kiwi (if needed)

Dinner – Beef vegetable stir fry – strips of beef, pepper, red onion, carrot and broccoli all stir fried in a wok. Enjoy with the probiotic side dish.

day six

Breakfast – Omelette or scrambled eggs with mushrooms

Lunch – Salmon dip with carrot sticks, pepper sticks and either courgette or cucumber sticks

Snack (3.30/4.00) – Banana & 4 brazil nuts (if needed)

Dinner – Chicken, prawn and mango curry with spinach through it, served on cauliflower rice. Stewed apple and cinnamon to follow.

And that is it! An all-round healthy diet with extra emphasis on the foods to help heal the gut. In brief, we:

- went gluten- and dairy-free;
- ate raw garlic via the olive tapenade recipe;
- ate 8 – 10 fruit and veg per day;
- ate sauerkraut 5 times per week;
- ate a rocket and radish salad 3 times per week;
- ate cabbage 5 times a week as sauerkraut, in juices or soups;
- removed white potatoes and white rice as they feed harmful bacteria in the gut;
- ate sweet potatoes / beetroot / turmeric mix 3 times per week as they feed beneficial bacteria (see prebiotic side dish recipe later);
- ate chicken bone broth in soups 3 times per week;
- ate stewed apple with cinnamon 3 times per week;
- exercised regularly;
- got a good night's sleep;
- improved our work/life balance;
- stayed hydrated; and
- were more mindful of our body's response to food.

We want to wish you good luck on your health journey. We hope that you have all of the information that you need to make positive changes that work for you.

However, if you are struggling and need extra advice please don't hesitate to contact us at **enquiries@thefoodphysio.com** where we can give simple advice or arrange a nutritional therapy consultation if needed.

ingredients & kitchen stocking

Listed below are just some of the foods that we kept regularly stocked in our cupboards and still do. We thought we'd list them here to make shopping for the first time a little easier.

basic stocking ingredients

Olive oil

Stock cubes – gluten-free Kallo

Passata

Coconut oil

Coconut milk

Gluten-free oats

Gluten-free oatcakes

Frozen berries

Cashews (not roasted or salted)

Almonds (not roasted or salted)

Walnuts (not roasted or salted)

Brazil nuts

Tins of wild salmon

Sunflower seeds

Pumpkin seeds

Sesame seeds

Linseeds (buy whole and grind at home, store in the fridge when ground)

Tinned tomatoes

Nut butters – cashew or almond (Meridian – Tesco or Amazon)

Soya milk (unsweetened)

Almond milk (unsweetened)

Lentils (not initially)

Tinned beans – cannelloni, kidney (not baked!)

Eggs

Rice noodles or courgette noodles

Vegetables – broccoli, cauliflower, peppers, courgettes, onions, kale, sprouts, tomatoes, mushrooms, spring onions, cabbage, beetroot

Starchy veg – sweet potato, turnip, carrots, butternut squash

Salad veg – mixed leaves, spinach / watercress / rocket mix. NOT iceberg*. Cucumber, cherry tomatoes.

Fruits – apples, pears, oranges, kiwi, strawberries, raspberries, blueberries, bananas, lemons

Herbs – coriander, basil, parsley, rosemary

Spices – turmeric, cinnamon, cumin, cayenne, garlic

Drinks – herbal teas (especially peppermint tea & green tea), carbonated water, red bush tea, decaff coffee

*iceberg is mostly water and does not have many other vitamins or minerals

top tip

When eating to improve your health you need to increase your fruit and veg intake. An easy way to do this is to switch your rice for cauliflower rice and your pasta for courgette strips, tastier than you might think and better for your health!

basic sauce recipes

You can just buy passata to use as a tomato sauce or coconut milk for a white one but these two recipes below are here to make your own sauces with much more flavour and can then be used like cook-in sauces that you buy in the supermarket. We make a batch lot and freeze them so that you can just take them out in the morning to use that night to make cooking quicker.

tomato sauce (passata)

This sauce is very adaptable for a variety of uses, for example, over meat, fish or vegetables, or as base for Bolognese or chilli con carne. Add bacon and it becomes Neapolitan sauce, or if you add curry powder instead of the oregano, it makes a nice tomato-based curry sauce.

Ingredients

2 large onions, chopped

1 teaspoon coconut oil

2 teaspoons dried oregano

2 tins chopped or peeled plum tomatoes

4 cloves garlic, crushed

500ml gluten-free stock - beef, chicken or vegetable

Method

1. Melt the coconut oil over medium heat in a large-based, non-stick pan and add the chopped onions. Stir and fry for 3-4 minutes until the onions have softened and gone translucent

2. Add the dried oregano (or curry powder) and fry off, stirring for a further 30 seconds, before adding the tomatoes, garlic and stock and bringing up to the boil

3. Then turn down to minimum heat on a small ring and gently simmer, stirring occasionally, for about 30 minutes. The sauce will eventually reduce to a thick paste consistency. If it goes a little too dry, just add a drop more water. When it is done you can blend it up to a fully smooth paste or leave the onions in chunks.

(dairy-free) creamy sauce

This is so similar to the above recipe and can be used to make a variety of other staple dishes. Again it can be used over meat, fish or vegetables, with ham and peas for Carbonara, or adding curry powder/paste instead of the basil, it makes a creamy curry sauce. Also, if you don't reduce it to thicken, it can form the base of a creamy soup like mushroom, chicken or fish chowder, or a Thai-style curry.

Ingredients

2 large onions, chopped

1 teaspoon coconut oil

2 teaspoons dried basil

2 tins coconut milk

250ml carton coconut cream

3 cloves garlic, crushed

2 gluten-free stock cubes or pots – chicken, fish or vegetable

Method

1. Melt the coconut oil over medium heat in a large-based, non-stick pan and add the chopped onions. Stir and fry for 3-4 minutes until the onions have softened and gone translucent

2. Add the dried basil (or curry powder/paste) and fry off, stirring for a further 30 seconds, before adding the coconut milk, coconut cream, garlic and stock cubes and bringing up to the boil

3. Then turn down to minimum heat on a small ring and gently simmer, stirring occasionally, for about 30 minutes. The sauce will eventually reduce to a creamy consistency. Don't let it go too far or it will separate. If it starts to, add a little soya milk.

top tip

Did you know?
Calcium is more easily absorbed by the body from spinach and broccoli than from milk or cheese

recipes to help the gut to heal

The recipes below relate back to the previous section on healing the gut and all have different reasons for helping your gut to heal itself.

sauerkraut

Ingredients

½ green cabbage

½ red cabbage

1-3 tablespoon sea-salt

Method

1. Chop finely or shred the cabbage and put it in a large bowl
2. Sprinkle over the salt
3. Massage the salt into the cabbage, liquid will start to come out of the cabbage. Continue massaging for about 10 minutes
4. Place the cabbage into a large bowl or put it into a fermentation crock
5. Put a plate on top of the cabbage and weight it down so that all of the cabbage is covered by liquid (I use a glass of water on top of the plate for this). If insufficient liquid has escaped from the cabbage add salt and a little water. The cabbage must be covered
6. Leave at room temperature for 2 weeks. More fluid will emerge from the cabbage, remove this as needed to prevent spillage. Taste, if this is the desired flavour then remove the plate and transfer the cabbage to sealable jars, ensuring that the cabbage is still covered by the salt water. Put it in the fridge to stop further fermentation. If the taste isn't quite right, leave it for up to 4 weeks.

This is the basic recipe, to add a bit of a different flavour you can add caraway seeds, shredded carrot or apple amongst other things.

prebiotic side dish

Ingredients

1 sweet potato

1 beetroot

1 large artichoke
(if available)

1 carrot

½ turnip

1 tablespoon coconut oil

1 clove garlic

1 teaspoon turmeric

Method

1. Chop all vegetables into small cubes
2. Crush the garlic and leave it for 10 minutes to release the active ingredient
3. In a frying pan, melt the coconut oil and throw in the chopped vegetables, the garlic and the turmeric
4. Fry for 10-15 mins and serve with any dish as a side, works well hot or cold

stewed apples

Ingredients

6 apples

3 teaspoons cinnamon

Method

1. Chop up the apples but keep the skins on
2. Put the apples in a pan with a lid and add about a centimetre of water to the base
3. Add the cinnamon and mix it
4. Bring to the boil then simmer for 10-15 mins until the skins are shiny, serve. Can be eaten hot or cold

top tip

Eating raw food preserves its enzymes so you get more from it. So increase your raw food consumption

chicken bone broth

Ingredients

Bones of 1 organic chicken

1 onion

1 clove garlic

1 carrot

1 stick celery

3 tablespoons apple cider vinegar

2 teaspoon turmeric (optional)

Method

1. Take bones of an organic chicken or organic beef bones and put them in a slow cooker. It doesn't have to be organic but if possible it's better for you! If you don't have a slow cooker use a pan on the stove and leave it during the day whilst you're in

2. Cover them with water and turn the slow cooker onto low

3. Add 3 tablespoons of cider vinegar – it helps mineral release from the bones

4. Add 1 chopped carrot, onion and crushed garlic

5. Add 1 piece of chopped celery and the turmeric if you like it

6. Leave on overnight and by morning you'll have a great bone broth

7. Sieve out the bones and the vegetables

8. Use it to make a soup or, if you're brave enough, have it as a drink!

9. Store it in the fridge once it's cooled if you're not using it straight away

references

Appleton N (2005) 'Stopping Inflammation – Relieving the Cause of Degenerative Disease'. Square One Publishers : USA

Challem, J (2010) 'The Inflammation Syndrome'. John Wiley & Sons: Canada

Cheney, G (1949) Rapid Healing of Peptic Ulcers in Patients Receiving Fresh Cabbage Juice. Calif Med Jan; 70(1): 10–15.

Collard, Dr P (2014) 'The Little Book of Mindfulness'. Octopus Publishing Group: China

Fasano, A (2012) Zonulin, regulation of tight junctions and autoimmune diseases. Annals of the New York Academy of Sciences. July 1258(1):25-33

Gibney et al (2009) 'Introduction to Human Nutrition'.

Gottschall, E (2012) 'Breaking the Vicious Cycle – Intestinal Health Through Diet'. Kirkton Press Limited: Canada

Jones, D.S (2010) Textbook of Functional Medicine. Gig Harbor: WA

Linus Pauling Institute (2019) https://lpi.oregonstate.edu/mic Oregon State University

Lipski, E (2012) 'Digestive Wellness'.

Liska et al (2004) 'Clinical Nutrition: A Functional Approach'.

O'Bryan, T (2016) 'The Autoimmune Fix'. Rodale: USA

Osiecki, H (2014) 'The Nutrient Bible'. Biocepts Publishing : Australia

Pizzorno, J & Murray, M (2008) 'The Clinician's Handbook of Natural Medicine'. USA

Weatherby, D (2004) 'Signs and Symptom Analysis'. Nutritional Therapy Association: USA

recipes

introduction to recipes

This is the recipe section of the book. It has been separated into sections so that you can easily find what you are looking for. Every recipe has the preparation time shown, the number of people that it is for and a simplicity ranking. A simplicity ranking of one indicates the recipe is quick and easy to make, whereas three is more difficult or more time consuming. Since this is a healthy eating book you will also see a fruit and vegetable quota, giving you an indication of how many of your 8-10 a day that you will be having if you eat a portion of the recipe.

At the end of each recipe there is a taste tip, detailing how you can alter the recipe slightly to get a different flavour or how to remove an ingredient that you are not keen on. Finally, there is information on how each recipe can help to boost your health. So, the 'back to health bonus' is shown which selects one ingredient and details how it can help to improve the way you feel.

We hope you enjoy preparing and eating them as much as we do!

Symbol	Meaning
	Preparation Time
	Fruit and vegetable quota per portion
	Simplicity
	Taste Tip
	Back to Health bonus

breakfast

breakfast

Breakfast can be hard when you're gluten and dairy free. However, once you get your mind-set away from the norm of cereal and toast you'll see it really isn't as hard as you think it is. Personally, I go for a juice or a smoothie depending on how much time I have in the morning. They always leave me feeling satisfied but fresh. Great if you're on the go as they're easy to take with you. I normally only have something solid at the weekend when I have more time to rest and digest.

A note about the difference between smoothies and juices. Smoothies retain the fibre as you blend all of the ingredients, so are best if you are wanting to boost your fruit and vegetable intake and relieve constipation. Juicing removes the fibre but retains the enzymes, vitamins and minerals. Since the bulk has been removed, the volume is less so you can drink more and get maximum nutrients into your diet. However, it won't help bowel movements. Choosing between one or the other depends on your health aims.

Remember, for breakfast to set you up for the day it needs to contain protein. That will help you to balance your blood sugar which helps with stress, prevents mood swings and aids energy levels and concentration. Hence, all of the breakfasts in this section have protein in them.

red berry breakfast smoothie

mins prep time

Ingredients
(for 2 people)

2 handfuls gluten-free oats

2 handfuls frozen berries

1 banana, peeled

2 tablespoons linseed, ground

450ml unsweetened almond milk

450ml water

Method
1. Put this all in a blender and switch on
2. Pour into a glass and drink

Lou's Taste Tips: To add an extra veg quota to this add 2 handfuls of spinach or kale. If you use kale make sure you blend it for a good 3-4 minutes to take out the bitty texture from the smoothie.

Back to Health Bonus: Oats contain beta-glucan which is a soluble fibre that boosts your immune system to help fight off viral and bacterial invasion. It's anti-inflammatory and can help heal wounds so is an all-round health bonus to include regularly in your diet. Caution though – you need to get gluten free oats to ensure that there is no cross contamination. Although oats are technically gluten free, they are typically grown in a field that has been used to grow gluten containing grains the year before. There is, therefore, the possibility of stray grain entering the oat crop if the field was not fully cleared.

strawberry, orange & banana smoothie

mins
prep time

Ingredients
(for 2 people)

2 handfuls frozen strawberries

1 banana, peeled

1 large handful spinach

1 large orange, squeezed

2 tablespoons linseed, ground

450ml almond milk

450ml water

Method
1. Put everything except the orange in a blender and switch on
2. Squeeze the orange separately to ensure no pips are in the juice
3. Add the orange to the rest
4. Pour into a glass and drink

 Lou's Taste Tips: You can exchange the strawberries for raspberries if you prefer and still get a really tasty smoothie. I always use frozen berries for this and not fresh, as the frozen ones have a more intense flavour and the cold makes the smoothie nicer to drink.

 Back to Health Bonus: Strawberries are a great source of vitamin C which is needed for multiple processes in the body. It's a natural anti-histamine, promotes healing, is essential for healthy gums and improves immunity amongst other things.

cherry & banana smoothie

mins
prep time

Ingredients
(for 2 people)

2 handfuls frozen cherries

1 banana, peeled

1 large handful spinach

2 tablespoons linseed, ground

450ml almond milk

450ml water

Method
1. Put this all in a blender and switch on
2. Pour into a glass and drink

 Lou's Taste Tips: If you're a nut lover you can add in some ground almonds to make it more filling, add 2 tablespoons if you'd like to try it.

 Back to Health Bonus: Cherries are packed full of antioxidants which help to mop up damage-causing free radicals whilst also being highly anti-inflammatory. Montmorency cherries are exceptionally good for any sufferers of gout and can reduce the frequency and severity of an attack. You can buy cherry liquid, add it to smoothies or drizzle it over some coconut yogurt.

zingy mango smoothie

Ingredients
(for 2 people)

2 handfuls spinach

2 handfuls frozen mango

½ lemon squeezed

2 tablespoons linseed, ground

450ml coconut water

450ml water

Method

1. Put this all in a blender and switch on
2. Pour into a glass and drink

Lou's Taste Tips: If this smoothie is too liquidy for you add a banana to thicken it up a bit. This will also add an extra portion to your veg quota.

Back to Health Bonus: Ground linseed is such a great health extra. It's an alternate form of omega 3 so, if you're not an oily fish loving individual then you can consume this regularly to boost your healthy fat levels. For women, it is also very hormone balancing as it binds to excess oestrogen in the system and therefore reduces pre-menstrual symptoms.

veggie smoothie

Ingredients
(for 2 people)

1 beetroot, peeled

1 carrot, peeled

2 apples, cored

½ lemon, squeezed

2 tablespoons linseed, ground

6/7 almonds

450ml almond milk

450ml water

Method

1. Put everything except the lemon in a blender and switch on
2. Squeeze the lemon into a dish to ensure no pips are in the juice
3. Add the lemon juice to rest
4. Pour into a glass and drink

Lou's Taste Tips: You can exchange the almonds for walnuts or cashew if you prefer them. Or, if it is filling enough, you could just leave the nuts out completely.

Back to Health Bonus: Lemons are packed full of vitamin C so are great to boost your immunity, prevent constipation and, as an added bonus, will help to keep you looking young! That's because vitamin C is needed to produce collagen which maintains skin elasticity.

detox heaven

I love this one! Great for detoxing but beware, it will make you pee more frequently so don't have it just before you go on a long journey!

Ingredients
(for 2 people)

2 apples

2 pears

2 carrots

2 beetroots

1 unwaxed lemon

⅓ cucumber

1 celery stick

2 inches broccoli stem

2 tablespoons linseed, ground

1 avocado, destoned

Method
1. Juice everything except for the avocado and linseed
2. After juicing, add the avocado and the linseeds
3. Blend it up and enjoy!

 Lou's Taste Tips: You leave the skin on the lemon here but if you don't like it quite that 'zingy' cut the peel off first.

 Back to Health Bonus: Beetroot is a great source of fibre, potassium and vitamin C. Not only are they associated with improved blood flow but they are also known to lower blood pressure and increase exercise performance.

green goddess

This is a deep green colour that just makes you feel so healthy! I enjoy starting the day this way.

Ingredients
(for 2 people)

2 apples

2 conference pears

2 handfuls spinach

½ pineapple

½ inch ginger

⅓ cucumber

1 celery stick

2 inches broccoli stem

2 tablespoons linseed, ground

1 avocado, destoned

Method

1. Juice everything except for the avocado and linseed
2. After juicing, add the avocado and add the ground linseed
3. Blend it up and enjoy!

Lou's Taste Tips: If you don't like one of the ingredients in here you could leave it out if you really wanted to but I doubt you'd be able to single the taste out from all of the rest. The only thing you have to leave in is the avocado, without this it's not filling enough to last you till lunch. You could try adding protein powder instead of the avocado but it really wouldn't taste as nice.

Back to Health Bonus: Raw ginger is a major natural anti-inflammatory but beware a little goes a long way. Adding too much will really add a kick to this smoothie. Health wise, it's also great to reduce nausea. However, it can also thin the blood so speak to your doctor if you're on blood thinners before you regularly include this in your diet.

pineapple & beetroot beauty

Ingredients
(for 2 people)

2 apples

½ pineapple

2 beetroot

½ lemon

⅓ cucumber

1 celery stick

2 inches broccoli stem

2 tablespoons linseed, ground

1 avocado, destoned

Method
1. Juice everything except for the avocado and linseed
2. Put the avocado in the juice and the linseeds
3. Blend it up and enjoy!

 Lou's Taste Tips: Pears taste really lovely with pineapple so if you're not keen on apples, put 2 pears in instead.

 Back to Health Bonus: Pineapple contains bromelain which is a superstar of nutrition. It helps to breakdown protein, it is anti-inflammatory, accelerates wound healing, reduces swelling and reduces blood clotting risk. Don't go overboard with it though if you take warfarin, as bromelain increases its affect!

orange delight

Ingredients
(for 2 people)

2 oranges, peel removed

2 carrots

2 apples

1 inch ginger

2 tablespoons linseed, ground

Method
1. Juice everything except for the linseed
2. Put the juice and the linseed in a blender
3. Blend it up and enjoy!

 Lou's Taste Tips: If you'd like to make it more filling add a banana or a tablespoon of ground almonds. Add either of these after juicing.

 Back to Health Bonus: Ginger is highly anti-inflammatory, oranges and carrots are high in vitamin C and linseed is high in omega 3's, so this is a great juice to reduce inflammation and boost immunity.

breakfast dishes

Now onto the non-liquid breakfasts! Some people prefer getting something solid into their belly's first thing and that's just fine. They don't necessarily take any longer to make, your choice of breakfast just depends on what you fancy and how much time you have.

fruit salad & seeds

For a quick easy breakfast that's still healthy look no further than this.

Ingredients
(for 2 people)

1 banana, peeled and sliced

10 strawberries halved with stems removed

1 kiwi, peeled and chopped

1 apple, cored and chopped

1 tablespoon pumpkin seeds

½ tablespoon sunflower seeds

½ tablespoon sesame seeds

Method
1. Put the fruit in a bowl
2. Sprinkle over the seeds
3. Add a dollop of coconut yogurt if you'd like to make it creamier

Lou's Taste Tips: If you fancy an extra crunch or would like to make it more filling add 8-9 almonds to the ingredients, plus if you really don't like one of these fruits leave it out and substitute it for another.

Back to Health Bonus: Kiwi is a great fruit to add to any recipe or just to enjoy on its own especially because it's low sugar. Packed full of fibre and vitamin C it's particularly helpful if you're constipated as this will help get you moving in no time! (Eat two a day to have maximum effect).

granola

Ingredients
(for 2 people)

1 handful blueberries

1 handful raspberries

2 tablespoons pumpkin seeds

2 tablespoons sesame seeds

1 handful almonds

2 tablespoons linseeds

2 handfuls gluten-free oats

2 tablespoons coconut oil

Method

1. Preheat an oven to 180°C
2. Mix the seeds, nuts, oats and coconut oil and place onto a baking tray
3. Bake for 10 mins
4. Allow to cool, throw on the berries and eat either with a little almond milk or coconut yogurt

 Lou's Taste Tips: Instead of adding blueberries and raspberries, stewed apple is a nice one to add to this as an alternative or, if you have a sweet tooth, you can add a tablespoon of honey to the dry ingredients before you bake it.

 Back to Health Bonus: Sesame seeds are packed full of calcium so a great alternate source if you're dairy free. However, it doesn't just end there, they also have high levels of iron, copper, manganese and magnesium, so provide essential minerals needed for every reaction in the body.

tasty banana & almond porridge with red berries

On a cold winter's day this is a really warming and welcoming dish. It may sound a little odd because there are no oats in it, but I would urge you to give it a go as it's pretty yummy!

mins
prep time

Ingredients
(for 2 people)

2 ripe bananas, mashed

115g ground almonds

225ml unsweetened almond milk (or soya milk)

½ teaspoon ground nutmeg

½ teaspoon ground cinnamon

227g frozen berries (mixed red, fruits of the forest, etc.)

Handful walnuts to garnish, broken up

Method

1. Put the frozen berries in a small pan with a splash of water on a low heat to thaw and heat up to boiling

2. Put the rest of the ingredients into a small pan and either blend with a hand-blender or mash with a fork – the blender will make a smooth paste whereas with the fork you can leave the banana bits coarser.

3. Warm through, stirring to prevent sticking and simmer away the liquid until it's reached the thickness you desire

4. Serve with the hot berries plus their juice on top, and scatter with the walnut pieces

 Lou's Taste Tips: This one's just fine how it is, however, if you've a sweet tooth you could drizzle a bit of honey over the fruit!

 Back to Health Bonus: Almonds are a magnesium powerhouse. Used for multiple processes in the body it's absolutely essential for health. It's needed for energy but is also a very calming mineral needed to help calm the mind to help you sleep. And if you're a headache sufferer magnesium is the key to making them go away as it dilates blood vessels. So, get almonds regularly in your diet and keep your levels topped up!

smoked salmon & scrambled eggs

An old favourite, great to enjoy as a late breakfast at the weekend but don't have this too often as smoked fish or meat isn't great for your health if eaten on a regular basis. Plus there's no veg quota in this so make sure you have a salad or soup for lunch and plenty of veggies for tea to compensate!

Ingredients
(for 2 people)

100g sliced, smoked salmon

3 fresh eggs

1 teaspoon coconut oil

100ml coconut cream

Salt and black pepper

Paprika

1 small handful fresh coriander

Method

1. Break the eggs into a non-stick pan with the coconut oil, cream and salt and pepper. Stir to break up the egg yolks over a low heat and keep stirring until the egg cooks and scrambles

2. Switch off the heat whilst the egg is still slightly runny otherwise it will overcook, go grainy and separate from the liquid. Serve on a warm plate, top with the smoked salmon, a sprinkle of paprika and the fresh coriander

Rich's Taste Tips: If you don't like fresh coriander (a love it or hate it sort of thing) then it has simply got to be freshly chopped chives. Delicious!

Back to Health Bonus: Salmon is a great source of healthy fat (omega 3s) needed to absorb vitamins A, D, E & K as well as being full of vitamin B12, sodium and selenium. Selenium's needed by your thyroid gland to boost your metabolism whilst vitamin B12 is essential for good nerve health. All in all salmon is a great source of nutrients especially when it's not smoked, so eat salmon often and smoked salmon occasionally.

savoury egg muffins

These are really easy to make in batches in cupcake tins and come out like fluffy, mini-omelettes. They can be served immediately or stored in the fridge (or frozen) and re-heated when required. There are many options for the principal flavours, or you can make up your own:

- Courgette and sun-dried tomato
- Mushroom, basil and onion
- Kale and chive
- Tomato and basil

- Yellow pepper and tomato
- Red pepper and spring onion
- Carrot and apple

Ingredients

114g in total of the main ingredient combinations (see above), finely chopped

1 tablespoon coconut oil

4 eggs, whisked together

Coconut oil for greasing

Salt - to taste

Method

1. Heat the coconut oil in a pan, then add the chopped vegetables and sauté them until tender
2. Cool the vegetables for 10 minutes, then mix with the whisked egg
3. Grease each cup of a cake tin with coconut oil using greaseproof paper and pour the mixture evenly into each recess
4. Bake for about 12-15 minutes in an oven at 180°C until the tops are firm or if an inserted toothpick comes out clean
5. Let them cool in the tin for a few minutes before removing. Serve immediately or store for later use

Rich's Taste Tips: This is a good one to spice up by adding a teaspoon of paprika to the basic mixture, or a ¼ teaspoon of chilli powder, or even a couple of finely chopped chilli's themselves.

Back to Health Bonus: Eggs are a really versatile food and a great source of protein to fill you up as a snack or a main meal. Protein is needed to build and repair cells, to transport nutrients and to speed up chemical reactions in the body. Eggs also contain sulphur needed by the liver to detoxify our bodies plus contain choline, selenium, vitamin A and vitamin D.

london classic
(smoked haddock, poached eggs, wilted spinach & hollandaise sauce)

Living in north east Scotland, I like to make this using Arbroath Smokie. Other types of smoked haddock are available – but this one's simply the best! Not classically 'London' I would accept, but a fusion of the best ingredients and recipes from across the UK!

Note: within this recipe, you have poached eggs and Hollandaise sauce which, pop them on top of a toasted, gluten-free roll with a slice of ham, and voilà, you also have the classic Eggs Benedict!

15 mins prep time

Ingredients
(for 2 people)

1 piece smoked haddock or Arbroath Smokie

2 eggs

Small bag spinach leaves

For the Hollandaise sauce:

4 egg yolks

Juice 2 lemons

250g coconut oil, melted

Pinch salt

Method

1. Whisk the egg yolks and lemon juice in a clear glass bowl until thickened and doubled in volume. Then place over a simmering pan of water on the hob, but make sure the water is not in contact with the bottom of the bowl (this is called a Bain-Marie)

2. Gently warm the mixture, whisking hard whilst also drizzling in the melted coconut oil. Keep whisking as the sauce warms and has doubled in volume again, then lift off the pan and finally stir in a pinch of salt. The Hollandaise should be thick, but smooth and satiny. Take care not to overheat as the egg will start to scramble. Set aside the bowl wrapped in a towel to keep warm for serving

3. Pop the Arbroath Smokie / smoked haddock into a non-stick frying pan with a little coconut oil to fry on both sides. In the meantime, you can use the simmering water from the Bain-Marie to poach the two eggs and wilt the spinach. Stir the water to create a whirlpool and crack in the eggs. They will take about 2-3 minutes depending on how soft or hard you like the yolks

4. Immediately the eggs are in, place a large sieve over the simmering pan containing the spinach leaves. Turn them with your hand until they wilt down in the steam. They will shrink significantly. Collect them into a ball and wring out any excess water into the pan

5. Serve the Arbroath Smokie / smoked haddock on a warm plate and lift out the poached eggs with a slotted spoon and place on top. Tear up the wilted spinach on top and pour over the warm Hollandaise sauce. Season with salt and black pepper

Rich's Taste Tips: Sprinkle some dried nutmeg, or finely grate some fresh if you have it, over the top before serving. The flavour goes very well with the Hollandaise sauce but beware, nutmeg is an acquired taste and you either love it or hate it. An alternative is a few fresh, chopped chives.

Back to Health Bonus: Spinach is a great source of vitamin A, K and folate plus magnesium which helps our muscles to relax, dilates our blood vessels, calms our minds and is needed for energy. It can be served hot wilted like in the above recipe or can be thrown into a smoothie to boost your veggie quota for the day.

top tip

Most people have heard about quinoa but maybe haven't tried to eat it yet. It's a great source of protein that's easy to digest and is cooked similarly to rice. About 15 minutes in boiling water should see it ready but you'll know as when it is you'll see the sprouts appear.

banana pancakes

My kids love these! And I must admit I do too! They are simply divine. You need to turn them cautiously on the first flip because they can break apart easily but once flipped they're easy to manoeuvre.

Ingredients
(Makes about 12-13 small pancakes)

2 large ripe bananas, peeled and mashed with a fork

4 eggs, whisked

Coconut oil for frying

Optional extras for topping:

Fresh fruit – blueberries & raspberries

Maple syrup or honey

Or all of the above

Method

1. Place the mashed bananas in a bowl and mix with the eggs using a fork. Get a non-stick frying pan hot, then add a small amount of the oil and put in two dollops of the banana pancake mixture on either side of the pan. If you use about 2 tablespoons in each, they should spread out to about 10cm diameter circle each.

2. Don't touch them and let them fry off on the underside for about 1 minute until firmed up and you can get a spatula underneath the edge. Shift them off the heat and work the spatula right underneath, possibly using another round ended knife to assist – they are quite delicate at this stage so be careful. Flip them over, return to the heat and cook the other side. You should be aiming for golden brown. Set aside on a warm plate in the oven and repeat for two more pancakes, etc.

3. Serve in two's or three's with whatever accompaniments you desire

Lou's Taste Tips: There are loads of optional extras that you can add to the mixture. Try ½ teaspoon ground cinnamon or nutmeg, dark chocolate chips, ground almonds or broken walnuts.

Back to Health Bonus: Packed full of potassium, bananas can help with blood pressure, nerve and muscle function and regulating water balance. Beware though, they're also high in sugar so great if you're about to work out but not good for balancing your blood sugar. Eat them with a handful of nuts if you want slower sustained energy release.

lunch

lunch

Lunch is just as important as any other meal of the day. In fact, if at all possible I would swap your main meal to lunchtime. It's better to consume more of your calories at lunch because you've more time to use them up. Too many people eat most of their calories within a couple of hours before bed. This gives us little chance to use up the energy generated from them and in the worst case scenario we put it all on as weight.

soups

Soup is a great way to get three portions of vegetables into your daily diet. The only downside is that unless it's a lentil soup or contains beans then there's no protein in it and even eaten with a slice of gluten-free bread it will leave you running on empty by late afternoon. So, if I make a soup without lentils or beans you'll always see quinoa added to it as a source of protein to make it more filling to improve your energy and stamina.

Now, a lot of people like bread with soup but gluten-free bread can be a little dry. I always opt for something different and swap bread for 2 or 3 gluten-free oatcakes or sprinkle a few seeds on top to give it a bit of a crunch.

If you like, you can always throw in a handful of spinach to increase your green veg intake as well.

top tip

Herbal teas are better than you think. As part of a nutritional programme they can be very helpful to improve digestion and optimise your health.

carrot & coriander soup

Ingredients
(for 4 people)

1 onion, peeled and chopped

6-7 carrots, peeled and roughly chopped

1 handful coriander, roughly chopped

1 clove garlic, peeled and crushed

400ml tin coconut milk

255g quinoa

1 dessert spoon coconut oil

1 gluten-free vegetable stock cube, dissolved in 1 pint of water

Method

1. Heat the coconut oil in a deep pan and fry the onion, stirring for 2 minutes until it goes transparent. Add the carrots and cook for about 4 minutes, stirring with the onion

2. Add the coconut milk, quinoa, crushed garlic and the stock cube to the saucepan, bring to the boil and simmer for 15-20 minutes until the quinoa is cooked. It will sprout little stalks out of each seed when it's done. At that point the soup will retain a bit of bite (lumpy bits of quinoa). If you want it smooth, just cook it for 5 minutes longer

3. Throw in the coriander just before you turn off the heat, blend with a hand blender and serve with gluten-free oatcakes

Rich's Taste Tips: You can get an extra richness in this soup, and also counteract the tartness of carrot on its own, by chopping and frying a handful of mushrooms with the onions at the beginning. Dried and re-hydrated cèpes will be fantastic, but just chestnut mushrooms from the supermarket will also work well.

Back to Health Bonus: Although coconut milk is high in saturated fat it is mostly in a form that is converted to monolaurin in the body which is highly antiviral and antibacterial so can protect from viruses and some infections. It is quickly converted in the liver, so is not likely to be stored as fat, plus it contains significant amounts of iron, magnesium, phosphorus, manganese and electrolytes to help balance fluid in your body. What more can you ask for?

roast parsnip & celeriac soup

mins prep time

Ingredients
(for 2 people)

4 parsnips, peeled and chopped into chunks

1 celeriac, peeled and chopped into chunks

1 large onion, peeled and finely chopped

2 teaspoons dried leaf tarragon

3 cloves garlic, peeled, smashed and finely chopped

½ punnet chestnut mushrooms, sliced

1 gluten-free beef stock cube or stockpot

1 litre boiling water

Sea-salt and black pepper to season

2 tablespoons coconut oil

Method

1. Pre-heat the oven to 200°C and melt 1 tablespoon of the coconut oil on a shallow tray. Toss the parsnip and celeriac chunks in the hot oil with a little salt and pepper, and put back into the oven for 25 minutes to start to brown

2. Meanwhile, in a deep wide pan heat the rest of the coconut oil on a medium heat and fry the onions and garlic for about 3 minutes, stirring until the onions go transparent. Then add the mushrooms and turn down the heat. Keep stirring the mushrooms for a further 4-5 minutes, then stir in the tarragon, stock cube or stockpot and add the water

3. When the roast parsnip and celeriac chunks are finished in the oven, add them to the stockpot, bring to the boil and then simmer for 15 minutes to fully soften the vegetables

4. Blend to a smooth paste, season to taste and serve

Rich's Taste Tips: Celeriac is quite a strong taste and if you don't like it, you can simply use four more parsnips, or four carrots. If you do like celeriac, go mental with the black pepper. The pepperiness really works with the strong flavour.

Back to Health Bonus: Celeriac is a rarely used vegetable yet contains a whole host of nutrients like vitamin C, K and B6, phosphorus and potassium. Vitamin K is known for its blood clotting effects but did you know that it's needed to help make strong bones, so a good supply is vital for anyone with osteoporosis or osteopenia.

mushroom, coconut milk & rocket soup

An extremely quick, easy, very rich and tasty soup for either an easy lunch or a crowd-pleasing dinner party starter. We do this one at least once a week just for a simple lunch, particularly in the winter when soups are the order of the day.

Ingredients
(for 2 people)

1 small punnet of mushrooms, sliced (field, button, chestnut)

1 large onion, chopped

3 cloves garlic, mashed

1 400ml tin of coconut milk

1 small packet of rocket or watercress

1 tablespoon coconut oil

1 tablespoon pumpkin or sunflower seeds for garnish

1 gluten-free stock cube

Method

1. Fry off the onion in coconut oil for 2-3 minutes over gentle heat until translucent and starting to brown

2. Add crushed garlic with stock cube / stockpot and fry-off for further 30 seconds

3. Add sliced mushrooms and fry for further 3-4 minutes until softened and also starting to brown

4. Add coconut milk, bring to boil and simmer for 3 minutes. Throw in the rocket (or watercress) and take off the heat to blend with a hand whisk to a smooth, fluid consistency

5. Return to the heat, just to bring back up to simmer, then serve in soup bowls garnished with seeds or a few more rocket leaves. Minimum effort, maximum taste!

Rich's Taste Tips: You can use watercress or spinach instead of rocket for this one (spinach is not as strong a flavour as the other two). For a lovely garnish, if you have got some, a swirl of truffle oil will really make this soup smell and taste very rich.

Back to Health Bonus: Your liver takes cholesterol out of your bloodstream and turns it into bile which is squeezed out into the gut to help digest fat in your diet. Eating bitter foods like rocket stimulate the flow of bile so should be a regular part of your diet if your cholesterol is a little on the high side.

roast cauliflower, onion & roast garlic soup

The roast garlic in this is really lovely, making it quite a rich soup.

Ingredients
(for 2 people)

1 cauliflower, chopped

1 whole garlic, tops chopped off

1½ tablespoons coconut oil

1 onion, chopped

400ml tin coconut milk

1 gluten-free vegetable stock cube or pot

500ml boiling water

Method

1. Put the garlic in a ramekin and put ½ tablespoon of coconut oil on the top
2. Roast it in the oven on 200 °C for 15-20 minutes. Keep an eye on it, if the cloves brown and start to lift out of the skins it's ready
3. At the same time, melt the rest of the coconut oil in a baking tray, then add the cauliflower and coat it in the oil
4. Cook the cauliflower for 20 minutes
5. Put the onion in a saucepan and fry off until clear
6. Put the cauliflower in the saucepan, squeeze the garlic out of the skins into the pan (plus the raw bits you cut off the tops with a garlic press) and add the coconut milk, stock cube and water
7. Bring it to the boil, blend and serve

 Rich's Taste Tips: A swirl of coconut cream and a sprinkle of paprika goes nicely on this soup.

 Back to Health Bonus: Cauliflower is a cruciferous vegetable which is needed by the liver to help remove toxins from our body. It's also a great source of vitamin C and K. So, to boost your immunity and help clear out those toxins, get more cauli in your diet.

tomato & basil soup

20 mins prep time

Ingredients
(for 2 people)

6 tomatoes, roughly chopped

400g tin tomatoes

200g quinoa

1½ tablespoons coconut oil

1 onion, roughly chopped

1 gluten-free stock cube, dissolved in 1 litre water

1 handful basil

Method

1. Put the onion into a saucepan with the coconut oil and fry until it is clear
2. Add the tomatoes and the quinoa to the pan
3. Top up with boiling water and add the stock cube
4. Bring to boil, then simmer for 15 minutes
5. Turn off the heat, throw in the basil and blend it up

 Lou's Taste Tips: The quinoa is in there to make this soup more filling and most importantly to help balance your blood sugar, but you can also achieve this by substituting the quinoa for a tin of cannellini beans.

 Back to Health Bonus: Basil is a real powerhouse as it contains antioxidants and is anti-inflammatory with high levels of vitamin A, C and magnesium. Enjoy it as part of a recipe like the one above or simply sprinkle it over fresh tomatoes covered in olive oil and seasoning.

top tip

The health benefits from garlic are only produced after you chop or crush it, so leave it for 10 minutes before you cook it otherwise you'll stop this from happening.

french onion soup with fried tofu

mins
prep time

Ingredients
(for 4 people)

700g onions, peeled, halved and thinly sliced

2 tablespoons coconut oil

2 tablespoons gluten-free flour

2 litres beef stock

1 teaspoon honey

300g pack Tofu to toast

Nutritional yeast (to taste)

Sea-salt

Chopped fresh parsley

Method

1. Put the onions in a heavy based non-stick pan with the coconut oil over a low to medium heat. Stir very regularly so they don't burn. They are ready when they are soft, sticky, sweet and deep gold in colour, you can even let them go towards dark brown. Add the honey at this point to help the onions caramelise

2. Stir in a couple of tablespoons of gluten-free flour, cook and stir for a further three minutes, then pour in the beef stock. Bring back to a simmer whilst stirring, then partially cover with a lid and leave to simmer for a good 45 minutes

3. Meanwhile, cut a decent sized chunk of tofu per person (or 2/3 smaller ones), sprinkle with salt and fry off in a bit more coconut oil, turning until lightly browned on all sides

4. When the soup is done, season, ladle into deep, heatproof bowls, place the tofu chunk on top and sprinkle with the nutritional yeast. Bake in a hot oven for five minutes or grill until the nutritional yeast has lightly browned. Top with the chopped fresh parsley to serve

Rich's Taste Tips: You can easily adjust the strength and richness of this soup by the amount you caramelise and brown the onions, but keep stirring regularly. Just doing them lightly makes a light soup if that's what you prefer.

Back to Health Bonus: Unless you're vegan you may not have heard of nutritional yeast. It's strange looking yellow flakes that add a certain nutty cheesy flavour to food. They're a great source of B vitamins needed for energy and now have added B12 which is really important to prevent nerve damage. In order to get the best of the B vitamins from nutritional yeast ideally make sure you add it to food after it's taken off the heat. However, that's not always possible depending on the dish.

curried cauliflower & apple soup

35 mins prep time

Ingredients
(for 6 people)

1 head cauliflower, chopped into chunks

3 apples, peeled, cored and chopped into chunks (pop them in water to prevent going brown until they are used)

1 teaspoon curry powder

4 cloves garlic, peeled, smashed and sliced

1 gluten-free chicken stock cube or pot

Juice 3 lemons

Sea-salt and black pepper

1½ litres water

250ml coconut cream

Parsley to garnish

Method

1. Put all of the ingredients, except the apples and coconut cream into a large pan with a lid, bring to the boil and turn down to simmer with the lid on for 20 minutes

2. Add the apples, get back to the boil and simmer with the lid on for a further 10 minutes

3. Add the coconut cream and blend to a smooth paste, season to taste and serve garnished with some chopped parsley

 Rich's Taste Tips: Add raisins if you like them, after blending, but then simmer them to re-hydrate for about 5 minutes and this will give an added sweetness and make this taste exactly like Coronation Chicken . . . . . bizarrely, as there's no chicken in it!

 Back to Health Bonus: 'An apple a day keeps the doctor away' used to be an often quoted phrase. Due to its high quercetin content which helps with allergies and its high fibre content (pectin) it adds bulk to your stool, binds to cholesterol in the gut and helps keep you regular. So, apples are an all-round winner!

chicken & vegetable soup

More of a stew / broth than a soup, this is best made using the leftover carcass of a roast chicken forming the stock (a bone broth - see earlier recipe for full cook times), and getting all the flavour and all the unused morsels of meat off the bone and into the broth.

(*this does not include the time to make the bone broth)

Ingredients
(for 4 people)

1 used roast chicken carcass with some meat remaining

Sea-salt and black pepper

5 cloves garlic, peeled, smashed and finely chopped

1 large onion, peeled and chopped

4 carrots, peeled and diced

2 parsnips, peeled and diced

3 sticks celery, chopped

2 teaspoons mixed herbs or Herbes de Provence

1 tablespoon coconut oil

Nuts, seeds and/or fresh basil to garnish

1 tablespoon apple cider vinegar

2 litres water

Method

1. Place the chicken carcass in a deep pan and fully cover with the water. Add a generous amount of sea-salt, some black pepper, the vinegar and all the garlic. Bring to the boil, cover with a lid, turn down to the lowest heat possible and simmer for at least 2 hours but longer if possible. Sieve out the bones

2. Heat the coconut oil in a large frying pan on a medium heat. Put the onions in first, stirring for a minute, then the rest of the vegetables and fry whilst stirring for a further 5 minutes. At the end, sprinkle in the mixed herbs. Add all this to the chicken stock pan, ladling a little stock out into the frying pan first, just to scrape off the frying juices to transfer back into the broth

3. Then systematically pull all the meat off all the different parts of the chicken carcass, dropping it into the broth and discarding the skin, gristle and bones. Bring back to the boil and simmer with the lid on for a further 20 minutes

4. Sprinkle with some nuts, seeds and fresh basil leaves

 Rich's Taste Tips: For an added bit of flavour put one heaped teaspoon of either paprika or cumin added at the end of the onion and fry for 30 seconds.

 Back to Health Bonus: As one of your 10 a day parsnip is a great one roasted for Christmas day and contains vitamin C, folate and manganese. Caution though, it is high starch and can feed bad bacteria in the gut, so keep it to a minimum if you've any wind problems!!

cullen skink

Another classic Scottish recipe, kind of a creamy smoked fish broth from the fishing town of Cullen on the north east Moray coast, made dairy free but still tastes amazing.

30 mins prep time

Ingredients
(for 4 people)

2 large pieces of smoked haddock, cubed into 2cm pieces

1 large onion, peeled and chopped

2 large carrots, peeled and chopped into small cubes

1 large sweet potato, peeled and chopped into small cubes

500ml fish stock (gluten free if using cubes)

250ml carton coconut cream

1 teaspoon coconut oil

Sea-salt

Handful fresh dill, chopped

Juice half a lemon

Method

1. Melt the coconut oil over a medium heat in a large, heavy-based non-stick pan. Add the cubes of carrots and sweet potato with a sprinkling of sea-salt and fry for about 15 minutes, stirring regularly until they are a golden brown on all sides and softened, but still with a bit of bite. Then add the chopped onion and fry for a further three minutes, still stirring frequently

2. Pour in the fish stock and most of the coconut cream and bring to the boil. Turn down to simmer and add the smoked haddock which will only take about 4 minutes to warm and cook through. Don't cook for too long or the chunks of fish will start to break up

3. Squeeze in the lemon juice, add the chopped dill, give it a quick stir and serve. Garnish with a sprig of dill and swirl of the reserved coconut cream

Rich's Taste Tips: Lime juice works well for this instead of the lemon juice, or a combination of the two. Similarly, fresh coriander will substitute for the dill, although I think the dill is very distinctive and is the key to the success of this dish, as well as being my main twist on the traditional Scottish recipe.

Back to Health Bonus: Dill isn't used terribly often in our house but as a great source of vitamin A and C it should be. Vitamin A is vital for eye health, reproduction and maintaining moist gut membranes which is essential for gut health.

roasted red pepper & tomato soup

Ingredients
(for 2 people)

2 red peppers, roughly chopped into large chunks

450g fresh tomatoes, roughly chopped

1 red onion, medium, roughly chopped

3 gloves garlic, peeled, roughly chopped

2 tablespoons coconut oil

1 teaspoon oregano

1 teaspoon salt

½ teaspoon black pepper

170ml stock

15oz tomato puree or passata

Chopped chives for garnishing

Method

1. Preheat the oven to 200°C with a roasting tray inside
2. Take out the tray and melt the coconut oil onto it, then toss the chunky peppers, tomatoes, onion, garlic, oregano, salt and black pepper onto the tray
3. Roast for 30 minutes, tossing again once at the halfway point
4. Put the roast veg into a pan with the stock and tomato puree and then blend with a hand blender until smooth. Heat up and slowly simmer for a few minutes. Serve topped with the chopped chives

Rich's Taste Tips: Any green herbs will go with this instead of the oregano – thyme, rosemary, sage, dried coriander leaves, tarragon.

Back to Health Bonus: Peppers are packed full of beta-carotenes that are converted into vitamin A in the body if needed. They provide a huge dose of vitamin C to help boost your immune system, vitamin E, B6 and folate. I eat them regularly as pepper sticks to dip in the salmon dip recipe in this book or houmous. Lovely!

veggie toast

Ingredients
(for 2 people)

200g button mushrooms, sliced

2 spring onions, sliced

6 sundried tomatoes, chopped

1 avocado, sliced

2 slices gluten-free bread or thin*

½ tablespoon coconut oil

*You can find bread thins in the supermarket, they are just squares of thinly sliced bread which are great for using as any kind of bruschetta type dish

Method

1. Fry off the mushrooms and onions in the coconut oil for five minutes
2. Add the sundried tomatoes and cook for a few minutes more
3. Toast the bread
4. Put half of the avocado on the base of each piece of toast
5. Share the mushroom mix between the two toasts

 Lou's Taste Tips: A number of other veg will work well in this, chopped and lightly fried, such as courgette, carrot or any colour of pepper, or even chopped, cherry or sundried tomatoes. I like the combination of leek, celery and red pepper with the avocado.

 Back to Health Bonus: The benefits of mushrooms vary depending on which variety you're eating but their medicinal benefits are well documented throughout the years. White mushrooms may not pack the biggest nutritional punch of the mushrooms but they're still a good source of B vitamins needed for energy, to support your stress systems and enable good nerve function.

hot smoked salmon salad

10 mins prep time

Ingredients
(for 2 people)

1 bag mixed leaves

8 cherry tomatoes, sliced

2 inches cucumber, sliced

2 spring onions, sliced

1 large piece hot smoked salmon

1 tablespoon mixed seeds

½ stick celery, sliced

Dressing

1 tablespoon olive oil

1 tablespoon balsamic vinegar

Method

1. Place two handfuls of mixed leaves on each plate
2. Put half of the sliced tomatoes, cucumber, onions and celery onto each plate
3. Flake the salmon and split it between the two plates
4. Sprinkle on the seeds, then the dressing

Rich's Taste Tips: I like to sprinkle smoked paprika over this one.

Back to Health Bonus: Being exceptionally high in vitamin K spring onion is good to help with blood clotting and essential for good bone health. It's also high in vitamin C and A so helps boost immunity and aid vision.

Caution: don't eat any smoked meat or fish on a regular basis, the smoking process produces carcinogens.

prawn, avocado & courgette salad

15 mins prep time

Ingredients
(for 2 people)

8 large cooked, shelled prawns

1 ripe avocado, destoned and sliced

1 large courgette, see Step 1

3 spring onions, chopped

Dressing:

1 clove garlic

2 egg yolks

Olive oil

Juice 1 lemon

Coarse sea-salt

Black pepper

Method

1. Shred the courgette into strips using either a grater or preferably a mandolin with a 'ribbon' attachment

2. For the dressing, peel the garlic clove, crush with the flat of a knife, back of a spoon or fork, roughly chop then briefly mash with the sea-salt using the back of a spoon, but leave some of the pieces of garlic in small chunks. Scrape into a bowl, add the olive oil, egg yolks, lemon juice and black pepper, stirring a little as you add each of them

3. Add the shredded courgette and chopped spring onions to the bowl, toss in the dressing, arrange the avocado slices and prawns on top, sprinkle with paprika and serve immediately. (Note: the salt in the dressing will start to leach water from the courgette if you let it stand, so eat immediately)

Rich's Taste Tips: If you fancy a little extra spice, sprinkle with a teaspoon of paprika (or smoked paprika) before serving, or alternatively mix it with the dressing.

Back to Health Bonus: Courgettes are a great source of fibre and really low in calories so are brilliant to add to any weight loss diet to help bulk out dishes. Being really versatile they can be eaten raw shredded in salads like above, fried in a little coconut oil, added to a ratatouille or even roasted with other veg!

duck breast, orange & quinoa salad

45 mins prep time

Ingredients
(for 2 people)

1 duck breast, fat trimmed off

2 large oranges (one of them with zest grated off)

100ml tamari soy sauce

100ml balsamic vinegar

1 teaspoon Chinese 5 spice

4 garlic cloves, crushed

1 inch fresh ginger root, peeled and finely chopped

4 tablespoons olive oil

Sea-salt

250g quinoa grains

Coconut oil

Method

1. Very thinly slice slice the duck breast (across-ways) and place it in a bowl with the orange zest, juice from the same orange, the Chinese 5-spice, crushed garlic, chopped ginger, soy sauce, balsamic vinegar, olive oil and a generous grind of sea-salt. Mix well, cover and place in the fridge for at least 4-5 hours (24 hours if possible)

2. When ready to cook, prepare the other orange by using a small, serrated knife and slicing off the top and bottom down to the fruit. Then slice off the rest of the skin just below the pith (also into the edge of the fruit). Go round putting the knife down each of the segments to separate the fruit, finally discarding the pithy bit which runs down the centre. Place the segments in a bowl and drain off any excess juice from the bowl or the chopping board into the duck marinade

3. Start the quinoa boiling in a pan of water. It will take about 15-20 minutes depending on whether you like it with bite or soft and fluffy. Meanwhile, lift the pieces of duck out of the marinade into another bowl using a pair of tongs or two spoons. Again, drain any excess juice off, back into the marinade – wait and do this a couple of times to get rid of most of the liquid, as you want the duck to fry, not boil

4. Place a large teaspoon of coconut oil into a non-stick frying pan and get it very hot. Add only enough duck pieces to be able to quickly flatten out across your pan base – too much and it will boil not fry. Because thinly sliced, they will cook and brown very quickly on one side. Flip each of them over and brown on the other side, then place on a warm plate in a 100 degree oven. You may need to do this in two batches depending on the size of your pan and amount of duck

5. Then put all the excess marinade into the hot pan, stir to scrape all the brown bits off the pan and simmer down until the sauce thickens into a syrup. Serve the cooked quinoa in piles on a plate, scatter over the duck pieces and orange segments, then drizzle each plate with the reduced, syrupy marinade juices

Rich's Taste Tips: I keep getting told off by Louise for this, but just because she doesn't like spicy, that doesn't mean you (or I) don't. One chopped red chilli! Put it, finely chopped with seeds and everything, in with the marinade. Lovely!

Back to Health Bonus: Everyone knows that oranges are packed full of vitamin C but did you know they also contain calcium and are yet another great source of fibre? So, if you have problems going to the loo this fruit is for you!

top tip

Watch out for soy sauce as it does contain gluten. You need to switch to tamari soy sauce which is gluten free

veggie wraps (alternative to sandwiches)

Ingredients

Options for the leaves / slices:

- Iceberg lettuce leaves
- White or green cabbage leaves
- Bok choy leaves
- Radicchio leaves
- Courgette slices
- Cucumber slices

Options for the fillings / toppings:

- Tuna-mayonnaise (lovely on cucumber)
- Ham and sun-dried tomato
- Chicken and avocado
- Or you can use any of the dips, pastes or relishes from our "Dips, Snacks & Finger-Food" chapter

Method

Instead of using bread, simply wrap your sandwich filling in a leaf. Alternatively use a leaf or thicker slice as an open sandwich.

Rich's Taste Tips: If you'd like a little change to the above recipe add a few drops of tabasco sauce on the tuna-mayo, or you could add a little soy sauce on the other filling options.

Back to Health Bonus: Swapping bread for a vegetable used as a wrap is a great way to increase your quota of fruit and veg for the day. Packed full of antioxidants to combat damage-causing free radicals in the body, these health boosting beauties can only help to optimise your health!

rice salad

mins
prep time

Ingredients
(for 2 people)

1 mug brown rice

6 cherry tomatoes, sliced

2 inches cucumber, sliced

1 tablespoon mixed seeds

2 boiled eggs, chopped

1 avocado, chopped

1 teaspoon garlic salt

1 teaspoon smoked paprika

1 tablespoon olive oil

1 teaspoon red wine vinegar

Fresh basil

Method

1. Cook the rice for 20 minutes in boiling water
2. Boil the eggs, shell them and cut them up
3. Add the chopped tomatoes, cucumber and avocado
4. Sprinkle over the seeds and mix with the garlic salt, smoked paprika, olive oil and red wine vinegar
5. Serve and garnish with chopped basil

Rich's Taste Tips: You can swap the eggs and avocado for peas and ham, salmon and spring onion or chicken and red onion, this is a great one for taking to work to have for lunch and can be prepared the night before and grabbed on your way out the door.

Back to Health Bonus: Brown rice is well known for containing B vitamins and being high in fibre but it's also high in manganese, magnesium and phosphorus. So, it's great for energy. However, make sure you soak it first and throw away the water before cooking as recent evidence suggests it may contain arsenic! Washing it should help to remove it.

grilled chicken waldorf salad

Ingredients
(for 2 people)

2 chicken breasts

1 pear, sliced

1 bag mixed leafs

Chopped walnuts

Dressing:

½ tablespoon olive oil

½ tablespoon white wine vinegar

Ground sea-salt and black pepper

½ small garlic clove

Method

1. Grill the chicken breast for about 10 minutes on each side on a low heat, or you can cook it in the oven on 180°C in a little water (to prevent it from drying out) for 35 – 40 minutes

2. Place 2 handfuls of salad leaves on each plate

3. Slice up the pear and lay it over the leaves

4. Sprinkle over the walnuts and then the dressing

5. Place the cooked chicken on the top and enjoy

Rich's Taste Tips: If you like an extra bit of crunch toss some pumpkin seeds and / or cucumber in with the salad leaves and dressing.

Back to Health Bonus: High in omega 3 & 6 fats plus protein, walnuts are highly anti-inflammatory and a great addition to any healthy eating plan. They also contain manganese, phosphorus and magnesium which help with multiple processes in the body. Sprinkle them on salads, on porridge or put them in smoothies to benefit from their goodness.

salmon tartar

This takes the classic Steak Tartar recipe but uses the juice of a lime to 'cure' both the raw salmon and egg yolk, and combine them with several guacamole type flavours into a very rich tasting starter. I would possibly not recommend super-sizing this into a main dish, purely because of how rich it is.

You will need a mixing bowl, a fork, a strong grip and plenty of elbow-grease for this one........but with ingredients containing several super-foods in their raw form, the task will simply become easier and easier the more times you prepare and eat this dish!

For the exhibitionists among you, if you chop all the ingredients ready into small pots, you can carry out the mixing and assembly of this next to your dinner party table to impress your guests with a flourishing display of culinary performance art!

Ingredients
(for 2 people as a main or 4 as a starter)

1 egg yolk

1 lime halved

1 large clove garlic

Smoked paprika

Sea salt

Black pepper

All finely chopped, i.e. 3-5mm chunks maximum size:

1 skinned salmon fillet

1 avocado (soft and ripe)

6 cherry tomatoes

2 spring onions

4 pickled gherkins

3 heaped teaspoons capers

Method

1. The only bit of non-mixing is to firstly crush and mash the garlic clove and sea-salt on a chopping board, using the back of a fork or spoon, and then scoop it off into your mixing bowl. Everything else then simply gets added in batches and mixed with the fork

2. Squeeze the lime juice in with the mashed garlic and salt and just lift out any lime pips which fall in (but they usually don't). Add the raw salmon and turn over with the fork so that the lime juice coats all around the small salmon chunks. The acidity will affect the protein within the fish, effectively 'curing' the raw meat

3. Then add the egg yolk and mix further. The egg yolk protein will also 'cure' and will thicken the whole mixture in consistency to help it stick together

4. Add the rest of the chopped ingredients (avocado, tomatoes, spring onions, capers, gherkins and chilli) one by one and beat them through the mixture with the fork. The avocado in particular will break down and thicken the consistency of the mixture further. This is where you start the need for elbow-grease to properly work the mixture!

5. Also then add and mix through the dill, coriander, smoked paprika, black pepper and some more sea-salt to taste

6. Finally, add the ground almonds and nutritional yeast flakes which thicken the final mixture to be moulded. Then

1 small chilli pepper (optional for a kick)

Small bunch fresh dill

Small bunch fresh coriander

3 tablespoons ground almonds

2 tablespoons nutritional yeast flakes

To garnish:

Any combo of salad leaves (lettuce, beet, rocket, spinach)

Olive oil (garlic, chilli or truffle infused)

Vinegar (white wine, apple cider or balsamic)

with a final flourish scoop out portions of the mixture and, one by one using two pallet knives, fashion them into round patties on a chopping board, and then transfer them onto your guests' serving plates. Garnish with the salad leaves and drizzle with oil and vinegar

Rich's Taste Tips: Finely chopped chilli works well with this, or you can substitute the raw salmon for raw fillet steak, but if so, change the dill and coriander for parsley and basil.

Back to Health Bonus: The benefits of coriander are numerous, between it's high content of vitamin A, vitamin K and it's ability to bind to toxins in the gut it's a good herb to include frequently in your diet.

top tip

You'll see no white potatoes in this book. They feed bad bacteria in the gut, are really high starch that throw out your blood sugar balance and don't have many vitamin & minerals compared to their sweeter counterparts. You can swap them in if you like but if you're trying to improve your health you'll get much more from sweet potatoes, butternut squash or turnip as an alternative.

egg quinoa salad

Ingredients
(for 4 people)

300g quinoa

3 eggs, boiled, shelled and halved

½ punnet strawberries, de-stalked and chopped

Bunch chives, chopped

All finely chopped:

2 tablespoons fresh parsley

1 yellow pepper

10 cherry tomatoes

10cm cucumber

2 tablespoons capers

6 small gherkins

2 sticks celery

2 tablespoons chopped fresh coriander

For the dressing:

1 teaspoon garlic salt

1 teaspoon paprika

2 tablespoons red wine vinegar

2 tablespoons olive oil

Method

1. Cook the quinoa until the little shoots start to appear, approximately 15-20 minutes
2. Drain the quinoa and leave it to cool
3. Add in all the chopped ingredients, then add the dressing and stir
4. Arrange the egg halves and strawberries on top, then sprinkle with chives

Rich's Taste Tips: You can substitute the green herbs for others, basil or dill, or the dried spices for others like cumin or ginger if you'd like to switch it around a bit.

Back to Health Bonus: You've probably heard of quinoa but did you know it's gluten free and a great source of protein? It's also full of fibre and multiple minerals so helps keep you regular, helps build and repair muscle and its minerals are used in multiple essential reactions in the body.

main meals

main meals

There are a mix of meals here, some quick and easy ones that we cook during the week when we've not much time and some more complicated for the weekend when we fancy something a little different and have more time to spend in the kitchen.

Sauces with the various meat and fish dishes are interchangeable to a certain extent so feel free to swap them around and see what tickles your taste buds.

Vegetable dishes can be used as accompaniments to meat or fish, or they make tasty and nutritional meals in their own right.

slow-cooked chicken with tomatoes, garlic & olives

This is a really simple but tasty dish we do quite often in the slow cooker. Alternatively, you can use a lidded casserole pot in a 110 degree oven.

*10 mins actual prep but 2-3 hours to cook

Ingredients
(for 4 people)

4 chicken breasts

400g tin chopped or peeled plum tomatoes

500g carton of passata

200g tin of anchovy stuffed green olives, drained

4 large cloves garlic, peeled and crushed

Sprinkling of dried, mixed herbs or Herbes de Provence

Method

1. Throw them all in the pot and slow cook for 2-3 hrs until the chicken breasts are tender. See - told you it was easy!
2. Serve with brown rice, quinoa and/or vegetables

Lou's taste tips: You can easily swap chicken out for turkey here if you fancy something different! Or have it with cauliflower rice to boost your vegetable intake for the day.

Back to Health Bonus: Everyone knows that chicken is a great source of protein but it's also high in selenium needed for good metabolism plus it's high in vitamin B3 and B6 which are needed for good energy levels.

beef & cashew rice noodle stir-fry

Ingredients
(for 4 people)

500g beef steak (fillet, sirloin, rump), thinly sliced or in small square-section strips

1 tablespoon coconut oil

2 large handfuls cashew nuts

1 large onion, peeled, halved, each half quartered then separate the layers

1 large carrot, peeled and julienned (basically small, stubby chips!)

1 green pepper, deseeded and cut into strips

450g ready-cooked rice noodles (or 300g dried and cooked according to their instructions)

For the marinade:

110 ml tamari (gluten free) soy sauce

110 ml rice wine vinegar

A dash Worcestershire Sauce

3 tablespoons sesame oil

3 tablespoons oyster or fish sauce

1 teaspoon Chinese Five Spices

4 cloves garlic, peeled and squeezed

2cm root ginger, peeled and finely chopped (or 2 teaspoons ground ginger)

Method

1. Mix the chopped beef with the marinade ingredients in a bowl, cover and leave in the fridge, preferably for 24 hours or for as long as you can. We've made this and cooked it on the spot sometimes, it just means the flavours don't get into the meat quite as much

2. When ready to cook, lift the meat out of the marinade using a slotted serving spoon and squeeze each spoonful with the back of another large serving spoon to get as much of the liquid out as possible (you want the beef to fry, not boil). Reserve the marinade as your sauce

3. Get a wok pan very hot, melt the coconut oil and quickly stir-fry the beef in batches, tossing it around using the two serving spoons. If it is sliced thinly it shouldn't take more than about one minute to brown and cook each batch. (If you add too much beef in one go, the wok will lose its heat and not be instantly evaporating any liquid, which is what leads to boiling rather than frying the meat. If that happens, stop, pour off the liquid, lift out the meat and start again)

4. Set aside the beef and then, adding a bit more coconut oil if necessary, stir-fry the other veg for 2-3 minutes to be cooked, but still a bit crunchy. Add the beef and the reserved marinade back in then as soon as they are up to the boil, toss the rice noodles though the whole mixture until coated and heated through

5. Serve in bowls with extra soy or sweet chilli for 'saucing'

Rich's Taste Tips: This stir fry works with any meat or prawns, but either beef or duck seem to absorb the marinade flavours better than anything else as they are quite coarse-grained meats. Experiment and see what you like most.

Back to Health Bonus: Good old beef gets a lot of bad press but if you choose lean cuts of grass fed meat you get a great source of protein, B vitamins, phosphorus, zinc and selenium. So, it's good for the skin, helps form active thyroid hormone needed to boost metabolism, helps repair muscle and maintain a healthy nervous system to name just a few benefits.

turkey burger with sweet potato chips

The burger meat in this recipe can easily be stored in the fridge or freezer for later use, or makes a nice stuffing for other white meats like turkey, chicken or pork.

Ingredients
(makes 8-10 burgers)

500g pack turkey mince

1 small onion, finely chopped

1 red pepper, finely chopped

3 cloves garlic, peeled and crushed

Ground sea salt and black pepper to season (minced meat seems to absorb salt and needs quite a lot to flavour it adequately, so be generous in the burger mixture)

2 large sweet potatoes, peeled or with skin on but scrubbed clean – cut into chips

1 tablespoon coconut oil

Gluten-free flour for burger "construction"

Method
1. Melt the coconut oil on a shallow roasting tray in a 200 degree oven. Toss the chipped sweet potatoes in the oil sprinkling generously with sea salt. Put in the oven for 20 minutes, then toss them again, then back in for a further 15 minutes to brown off evenly
2. Meanwhile, mix all other the burger ingredients in a bowl, sprinkle some gluten-free flour on a board, and then put a large tablespoon sized dollop of the mixture onto the floured surface. Rub some more flour on your hands and fashion the mixture into a circular pattie. Don't make it too thin (keep about 2cm thick) or it will break up on cooking. Repeat until all the mixture is used up
3. To seal the burgers and stop them from breaking up, heat some more coconut oil in a wide based non-stick frying pan and when it's really hot, use a flat spatula to scoop and place the burgers in the pan. Fill the pan but leave 2cm between each burger, so you may need to do two batches. Don't try to turn them for at least a minute as this will allow the undersides to seal. Turn with the spatula (it sometimes helps to use two spatulas to sandwich the burgers between) and cook for a minute on the other side
4. Transfer the sealed burgers to a roasting tray in the oven for the final 10 minutes that the sweet potato chips are in there
5. Serve on a gluten-free bun with the sweet potato chips, mango salsa (see Page 99) and any kind of salad

 Lou's Taste Tips: If you fancy changing the flavour a bit try adding paprika (1 heaped teaspoon) and/or ground cumin (½ teaspoon) to the burger ingredients before mixing.

 Back to Health Bonus: Sweet potatoes are a brilliant alternative to white potatoes and are full of beta-carotenes which are converted by the body into vitamin A. So, if you want to boost your immune system, help keep your eyes healthy or your gut membranes moist, so they do their job properly, then this is the food for you!

chicken paprika with sun-dried tomatoes

20 mins prep time

Ingredients
(for 2 people)

2 chicken breasts, cut into thin strips

10-15 sun-dried tomatoes, cut into strips

1 medium onion, finely chopped

4 cloves garlic, crushed or finely chopped

250g button mushrooms, halved or quartered depending on size

1 gluten-free chicken stock cube or stockpot

2 heaped teaspoons paprika

1 flat teaspoon nutmeg

400ml tin coconut milk

1 tablespoon coconut oil for frying

Juice ½ lemon

Fresh basil leaves, torn into small shreds

Either cauliflower or courgette for rice or noodles to serve with

Method

1. Put the coconut oil in a frying pan and stir-fry the chicken strips, stock and garlic on high heat for a few minutes until starting to brown. Set aside

2. Add some more coconut oil to pan and stir-fry the onion and sun-dried tomato for a minute until the onions are translucent, then add the mushrooms and stir-fry for a further 2 minutes

3. Turn off the heat and stir in the paprika and nutmeg, then add the part-cooked chicken strips back in with the tin of coconut milk and lemon juice

4. Bring back to the boil and simmer for about 10-15 minutes stirring occasionally to prevent sticking. The chicken will cook through and the coconut milk will reduce to a creamy sauce consistency. Don't let it go too far or the sauce will start to curdle (you can add a little more coconut water, soya/almond milk, or just water, to keep the consistency right)

5. Scatter in the fresh basil leaves and serve either on cauliflower rice*, courgette pasta or with any of the vegetable accompaniments

*Cauliflower rice is simply steamed cauliflower that has been mashed up to resemble rice

Rich's Taste Tips: Instead of chicken, use turkey or pork, or even fish or king prawns. If using fish or prawns, don't pre-fry and just add 8 mins to the cooking time in the sauce for fish at the end and 3 mins for prawns.

Back to Health Bonus: Paprika is high in vitamin A, iron and B vitamins so it's good for healthy vision, for good red blood cells and for a healthy nervous system.

venison stew

Living in Scotland, venison is easily available but, depending on the source, it can be a bit on the tough side if not prepared properly. The slow cooking in this recipe sorts out even the toughest of meats. Pheasant or stewing beef work very well done in the same way.

*20 minutes actual preparation and 4-5 hours in the oven or slow cooker

Ingredients
(for 4 people)

500-800g venison, trim off any fat you can see and cube to 3cm

4 heaped tablespoons gluten-free flour

3 teaspoons paprika

12 dried juniper berries, ground

1 teaspoon coconut oil

500ml gluten-free beef stock

300ml carton passata

4 cloves garlic, peeled and finely chopped

1 large onion, peeled and roughly chopped

1 large carrot, peeled and roughly chopped

1 large parsnip, peeled and roughly chopped

1 large celery stick, roughly chopped

Method

1. Put the flour, paprika and ground juniper in a bowl and mix evenly. Then toss the venison cubes in the mixture until coated on all sides

2. Heat the coconut oil in a hob-proof ceramic casserole dish or frying pan and seal the outside of the floured venison until brown on all sides. You might need to do a couple of batches, then set them aside

3. Then fry off the chunky vegetables and chopped garlic in the oil from the meat. Stir them, as the moisture that comes out of them will help you to scrape all the meat brownings off the sides and base of the pot

4. When the vegetables have softened a little, turn off the heat and mix in the residual flour, paprika and juniper. This will help to thicken the stew. Stir in the beef stock and passata, put the lid on the casserole dish (or transfer to a casserole dish if you used a frying pan) and cook in a low oven (110 °C) for about 4-5 hours. Or put it all into a slow cooker. Serve with boiled or mashed sweet potatoes and broccoli

 Rich's Taste Tips: Fruit actually works really well with meat, dark meats in particular. Simply throw in any of the following (stones or pips removed) for the stewing with the lid on: 15 prunes; 12 apricots or plums; 4 peaches, nectarines or small apples; a large mango (peeled); or even 3 oranges (peeled and split into segments). They will give a nice flavour, as well as a sweetness and richness to the stew, to compliment the flavour of the dark meat.

 Back to Health Bonus: Venison is a great source of low fat protein that's also packed full of iron, a multitude of B vitamins, phosphorus, zinc and selenium so boosts red blood cell formation, helps body tissue repair, aids thyroid function (selenium) and is good for the skin (zinc).

pan-fried duck breast in a red-berry jus

Ingredients
(for 4 people)

4 duck breasts, fat on

Sea-salt and cracked black pepper

2 tablespoons coconut oil

2 large sweet potatoes, skins scrubbed and cut into chips

300g mixed red berries or fruit of the forest, defrost in advance if frozen

1 gluten-free beef stock cube

1 tablespoon honey

1 clove garlic, peeled and crushed

4 spring onions, sliced across diagonally

1 head broccoli or between 12 and 16 spears asparagus

Method

1. Prepare and season the duck breasts in advance. I prefer the fat completely removed but Richard likes some left on and fried crispy! If you have any inflammatory problem though I would recommend you take it off as it will make inflammation worse, so Richard avoided this when he was ill. If you do want to keep it on, put the breasts fat-side down on a chopping board and trim the excess fat from around the edges. Flip the breasts over and score the fat diagonally in half cm lines then do the same at 90 degrees on the other diagonal. Finally, season both sides of the breasts with salt and pepper and rub in with your fingers. Put a little more salt on the fatty sides as this will help it to crisp up.

2. Melt 1 tablespoon of coconut oil on a roasting tray before adding the sweet potatoes. Roast for 25 minutes then turn and roast for a further 15 minutes

3. After choosing which green vegetable you like, place it in a steamer and cook for 15 mins.

4. Whilst the vegetable is cooking, melt the coconut oil in a wide-based, non-stick frying pan and then fry the duck breasts. Timing is everything! If you have fatty sides to crisp up, these will take about 3-4 minutes on their own on a high heat first – check for the fat going golden brown all over. Then for the meaty sides, turn down to a medium heat and you want about 3 mins for well-done, 2 mins for medium and 1 min for rare. If people want different things, with and without fat, this will be a Krypton Factor challenge (showing our age there) in its own right to calculate all the timings – but you can do it! When the breasts are cooked, place on a warm plate in a 100 degree oven for 7 minutes to rest and pink through evenly (turn down oven after sweet potatoes are done)

5. To make the sauce, put the crushed garlic and chopped spring onion into the hot pan and fry off for 30 seconds, stirring vigorously. Then add all the other sauce ingredients, bring to boil and turn down the heat to simmer whilst the duck breasts are resting. The berries and sauce should reduce to a sticky, but not too thick, consistency

6. When the 7 minutes are up, either serve the duck breasts whole or slice them diagonally and arrange on the plate. Drizzle with the sauce, put the remainder in a warmed jug for people to help themselves and serve with vegetables and sweet-potato chips

Rich's Taste Tips: Chestnut mushrooms or cèpes, finely chopped and fried off with the spring onions will give a lovely richness to the sauce.

Back to Health Bonus: Duck is another great source of protein, B vitamins, iron, selenium and phosphorus. Phosphorous isn't talked about very often but it's essential for bone growth, bone health and for producing energy.

top tip

Just one serving of kale gives 6 times your daily requirements of vitamin K important for blood clotting, twice your vitamin A requirements needed for good eyesight and your vitamin C too. It's extremely anti-inflammatory and is high in antioxidants that combat damage in the body, a real winner!

chicken, prawn & mango wok curry

This is a great family favourite, the kids love it.

I find it helps to prepare all of the ingredients into little bowls (grouped as per the recipe) to add quickly as necessary so you can keep stirring and make sure nothing sticks.

Ingredients
(for 4 people)

3 chicken breasts, in thin slices or strips

1 bag large prawns

1 large, ripe mango, cut away from the stone and skin and then cubed

5 large cloves garlic (yes, it's garlicky, but that's how we like it!) – skinned, smashed and finely chopped

2 inches root ginger, peeled and finely chopped

2 teaspoons curry powder (use mild, hot, Thai - whatever you fancy)

2 teaspoons turmeric

1 gluten-free chicken stock cube

1 tablespoon honey

3 limes, zest grated, halved and squeezed

400ml tin coconut milk

150ml carton coconut cream

1 large teaspoon coconut oil

240g brown rice

Fresh coriander and any kind of sweet, spicy chutney to serve

Method

1. Put the coconut oil in a wok and get it very hot. Throw in the chopped garlic and ginger, stir for about 20 seconds, then take off the heat. Crumble in the stock cube and stir in the curry powder and turmeric. Stir for 30 seconds and the residual heat in the wok should fry off the spices nicely. Add the honey, put back on the heat and get it bubbling, then squeeze in the lime juice. Add the zest and finally the tin of coconut milk and carton of coconut cream

2. Add the chicken to the sauce, turn down the heat and simmer for about 15 minutes. This is the secret with this dish, that the meat is not fried at all. It is purely poached in the sauce, which, providing it is not poached for too long, ends up with very tender chicken pieces

3. After 15 minutes, the chicken should be cooked nicely, and the sauce should have reduced to a typical thick curry sauce type consistency. At that point, add in the mango pieces and the prawns and bring the whole thing back to a simmer. As soon as it is simmering, the dish is complete. Turn it off and serve. If you boil the sauce any longer, the mango will become too soft, and the prawns too hard

4. Serve with brown rice, a sprinkling of fresh coriander leaves and sweet, spicy chutney on the side

 Rich's Taste Tips: This is a great one to throw in two handfuls of spinach to increase your veg quota for the day or you could eat it with cauliflower rice! (Cauliflower rice is simply steamed cauliflower that has been mashed to resemble rice)

 Back to Health Bonus: If you've any kind of inflammatory joint problem then turmeric is a must for you. Research has shown it can help reduce pain and swelling yet is kind to the stomach unlike other anti-inflammatories. It helps to improve liver function and has been shown to have anti-cancer effects, a real spice powerhouse!

turkey mince & courgette moussaka

mins
prep time

*40 minutes actual
preparation and 20 minutes
in the oven

Ingredients
(for 4 people)

500g turkey mince

2 tablespoons coconut oil

1 onion, peeled and finely
chopped

4 cloves garlic, peeled and
finely chopped

Tin chopped or peeled plum
tomatoes

Sprinkling dried oregano

1 gluten-free chicken stock
cube or pot dissolved in
500ml boiling water

3 large courgettes, sliced
diagonally about ½cm thick

4 pinches ground sea-salt
and more for salting the
courgette slices

3 heaped tablespoons
gluten-free flour

550ml almond milk

5 tablespoons nutritional
yeast flakes

2-3 tablespoons olive oil

Method

1. Fry off the turkey mince, with the sea salt and coconut oil on a high heat in a large, non-stick frying pan, stirring occasionally to break up and until the mince is nicely brown all over

2. Remove the mince from the pan. Then soften the chopped onion and garlic with a little more coconut oil on a medium heat. Add the mince back in along with the tomatoes, oregano and stock, bring back to the boil then turn down to simmer for about 25 minutes. Stir occasionally until the fried mince has absorbed all the water and the tomato has reduced to a thick sauce

3. Meanwhile, the courgette slices can be salting to remove excess moisture. Arrange them on large dinner plates and sprinkle with salt, leave standing for about 10 minutes then flip them over and do the same on the other side. After that, wash all the salt off each slice and shake dry or pat with kitchen towel

4. Then using another wide, non-stick frying pan, get about a tablespoon of coconut oil very hot and add enough courgette slices to cover the bottom of the pan. They will take about a minute to lightly brown then flip them over to brown the other side. Set aside and repeat in batches for all the courgette

5. The final layer is the white sauce. Put the flour in a saucepan and, using a wooden spoon, keep mixing in small amounts of olive oil until it forms a slightly runny paste. Then mix in small amounts of the almond milk until the mixture is liquid enough that you can simply pour in the remainder of the milk. Place on a medium heat, stir the bottom of the pan constantly until the sauce thickens. You may have to lift off the heat and stir more vigorously to stop it lumping just as it reaches the thickening point. Finally, stir in most of the nutritional yeast

6. Then put the Moussaka together. Just layer up the mince, the courgettes and the white sauce in an oven-proof dish. Repeat to do a second layer and then top off with a final sprinkling of nutritional yeast flakes. Cook through in a 180 degree oven for about 20 minutes and serve with salad

Rich's Taste Tips: Beef mince and aubergine can be easily substituted here to make the more traditional Moussaka, but we quite like the flavours in this one. You could also substitute the meat layer for our Ratatouille Vegetable Accompaniment recipe to make this a veggie main meal.

Back to Health Bonus: Turkey is a great source of low fat protein needed to build and repair tissue within the body, needed to make enzymes which speed up essential reactions in the body and for the proper functioning of the immune system. If you don't get enough the body starts to breakdown your muscle to use instead, so it really is vital for good health!

coq au vin blanc

The simplicity of this dish is its secret. Normally with red wine but white is more delicate in its flavours. We lived in France for a time and I tried enhancing the recipe with various additions, but it never seemed to work as well as just the simple basic ingredients. The French farmer's wife would traditionally have used this slow pot-roasting as a method of using up older chickens, which naturally have tougher meat, when their egg-laying days may be coming to an end. Hence the title "Coq" rather than "Poule" or "Poulet" which in French describes a younger chicken (as in the English name "Pullet").

*15 minutes actual preparation and 2 hours cooking

**Can be increased with veggies added to accompany it!

Ingredients
(for 4 people)

1 whole chicken, quartered, with skin on (or 8 chicken thighs)

12-16 shallot onions, plunged in boiling water for 1 minute, cooled then peeled but leaving the root stub on each onion (that way they will stay whole)

250g button mushrooms, halved or quartered into large chunks

3 large carrots, peeled and cut into large chunks

6 cloves garlic, smashed with the flat of a knife-blade and roughly chopped

2 gluten-free chicken stock cubes

Method

1. Sprinkle and rub into the chicken skins the salt, pepper and paprika. In a large, heavy, iron casserole pot, on the hob at first, melt the coconut oil until hot and then place in the chicken pieces. You may need to do two batches. Brown off the outside of the chicken until the skin has crisped, turning to do all sides, then set aside on a plate

2. In the hot fat that will have come out of the chicken skins, throw in the shallots, carrots and mushrooms and keep stirring as they fry off the outsides for about 3 minutes. Then add the garlic and stir-fry for another minute. Finally, sprinkle in the flour and one stock cube, and stir to coat round the vegetables and fry for about 30 seconds

3. In a saucepan, add the second stock cube to 375ml of boiling water, then add the lemon juice, stir and bring back to the boil. Turn off the heat. Return the chicken pieces to the original pot and push it down. Pour the stock over the chicken so that they are about two thirds covered by the liquid. It doesn't matter if some bits are exposed, they will just brown a little more

4. Put the lid on the casserole pot and place in a 160º oven for around 2 hours. Serve simply with brown rice, cauliflower rice or sweet potatoes and vegetables

1 flat tablespoon gluten-free or rice flour

375ml water + juice of 2 medium sized lemons

1 tablespoon coconut oil

Salt and black pepper

Paprika

Rich's Taste Tips: You may have spotted this Coq au Vin Blanc doesn't actually contain any Vin Blanc! Being a healthy eating cook-book, I was banned by Louise from including any alcohol (although my scientific assertion would be the alcohol boils off anyway and all you are left with is fruit sugars and flavours, but I suppose there could be other chemicals used in the production, so I'll have to concede on that basis). The use of stock plus lemon juice in this recipe instead is a way I've discovered of recreating the same sort of flavours as a reduction of white wine in a sauce.

Back to Health Bonus: Carrots are packed full of beta-carotene, a nutrient that is converted by your body into vitamin A as required. It's needed for good vision, hence the old story of eating carrots to help you see in the dark! High levels of carotene have also been shown to reduce the risk of chronic disease including cancer, so get more brightly coloured fruit and veg in your diet.

lamb bhuna

mins
prep time

*30 minutes actual preparation and 80 minutes - 4 hours cooking depending on method (see 4. below)

Ingredients
(for 4 people)

Dry Spices for Grinding:

2 teaspoons whole coriander seeds

1 teaspoon whole cumin seeds

1 teaspoon whole mustard seeds

1 teaspoon whole fennel seeds

1 teaspoon whole fenugreek seeds

1 teaspoon black peppercorns

1 tablespoon coconut oil

1 large onion, finely chopped

2-3cm piece fresh ginger root, very finely chopped

4 cloves garlic, finely chopped

2 whole red chillis, finely chopped

2 large tomatoes, peeled and chopped (or 100g tinned chopped or plum tomatoes)

500g diced lamb, preferably leg meat

Sea-salt

100ml just boiled water

Method

1. First of all, make your own curry powder from the dry spices. Get a frying pan hot, put in all the dry ingredients and keep stirring until they darken in colour, but don't blacken. Put them aside in a small dish to cool and then, using a pestle and mortar, grind them to a powder. You can make batches of this and store for later use

2. Melt the coconut oil in a heavy, iron, non-stick casserole dish on the hob (but use one with a lid available). Add the chopped onions, ginger, garlic and chillis, and fry for 4-5 minutes, stirring until nicely browned

3. Then add the tomatoes, get them bubbling and keep stirring until reduced to a thick paste. Stir in the powdered spices and cook for a further minute. Add the diced lamb and sea-salt to taste (I like my curries quite salty to off-set the spiciness.) Cook the lamb whilst continuing to stir for a further 5 minutes. Finally, stir in the 100ml of boiled water and bring the whole thing back to a simmer and put the lid on

4. There are then two options for the main cooking. If you haven't quite as much time for advance preparation, just simmer gently on the hob on a very low heat for about 80 minutes until the lamb is tender. You will need to stir occasionally just to make sure the base is not sticking and burning. My preferred method is to slow cook in a very low oven (about 120º) for around 4 hours. You get much more even cooking without the risk of burning, and I think it makes the lamb even more tender

5. Before serving, just check there isn't too much liquid still in the curry. When you stir, the sauce should be a kind of paste and cling to the meat. If there is too much liquid, just pop it back on the hob without the lid and fast reduce, stirring continuously until you get to that clingy consistency. Serve simply with brown rice and some gluten-free naan bread

Rich's Taste Tips: As per any Indian restaurant menu, you can simply make this a beef or chicken bhuna instead, although I do think there is something about lamb that works well with this recipe more than other lighter curry sauces. I don't know why – maybe it is just the dark / light colour association!

Back to Health Bonus: Lamb is not a meat we eat very often due to its high fat content which is inflammatory but if eaten occasionally it's still a good source of protein, zinc, selenium and most B vitamins, especially B12 so helps with good nerve function, good skin, your thyroid and helps with energy production.

fillet of beef with creamy cèpe sauce

Absolutely gorgeous and totally gluten and dairy free! I promise you, once you have tried this, you will not want to go back to cheese or cream sauces with your steak.

If your kids baulk at the sight of mushrooms like ours, grind the dried cèpes to a powder in a coffee grinder or food processor before using them.

Ingredients
(for 2 people)

2 fillet steaks, in thick slices or in cubic chunks (depending on your appetite for pinkness)

2 tablespoons coconut oil

Dash olive oil

400ml tin coconut milk

Juice 1 lemon

A handful dried cèpe mushrooms (known as porcini in Italy, Karl Johanns in Scandinavia and Penny Buns in Great Britain)

1 gluten-free beef stock cube

2 cloves garlic, crushed

Sea-salt and ground black pepper

Fresh parsley or coriander to garnish

½ head broccoli, broken into florets

1 large sweet potato, peeled and cut into fries

Method

1. Take the beef out of the fridge an hour before cooking to come up to room temperature. Cut into desired size and shape of steaks, and rub with olive oil, sea-salt and black pepper
2. Melt 1 tablespoon of coconut oil on a baking tray in the oven set at 180°C, add the sweet potato to it and coat it in the oil. Cook for 20 minutes, turn them over and cook for a further 20 minutes
3. Meanwhile, about half an hour before, put the coconut milk, lemon juice, dried (or powdered) cèpes, stock cube and crushed garlic into a saucepan and bring to a gentle boil. Simmer for about twenty minutes, stirring occasionally, until reduced and the sauce thickens to a consistency that is still runny but will coat the back of the spoon (basically, aim for double cream). Turn off the heat and leave to stand – the cèpes will continue to work their magic in the warm sauce
4. Put the broccoli on to steam for 15 minutes
5. Have a warming plate ready in a 100 degree oven and, with about 10-12 minutes to go, add 1 tablespoon of coconut oil to a hot frying pan and cook the steaks whilst timing: for Well Done 3 minutes each side; for Medium 2 minutes each side; and for Rare 1 minute each side
6. Place the steaks on the warm plate in the 100 degree oven for about 5-7 minutes to fully pink through and relax the meat. Meanwhile pour the cèpe sauce into the frying pan to combine with the remaining beef juices, scrape any browned bits into the sauce and warm to a simmer
7. When times up, add any juices which have exuded from the beef on the plate in the oven to the sauce in the frying pan. Serve the sauce over the steaks. Garnish with some fresh parsley or coriander and this goes fantastically with just some simple roast veg and the broccoli

 Rich's Taste Tips: Don't meddle with this one, it's lovely as it is!

 Back to Health Bonus: Olive oil is highly anti-inflammatory being one of the good fats that we need to eat regularly to maintain good cell membrane health. Eat it often to help with skin, decrease pain from arthritis and help with your heart. So get some on your salad as a dressing with a little balsamic vinegar.

sticky chicken with lime & basil rice

We were 'experimented on' with this dish by a French chef called Norbert who we know from a little restaurant close to where we lived in France. In fact, he coupled the Chinese-spiced sticky chicken with an Italian creamy, parmesan risotto, which seems an odd combination, but actually worked really well. However, here we have simply presented it with a lime and basil rice to keep it dairy free and maintain the south east Asian theme throughout the dish.

Ingredients
(for 4 people)

2 large (or 3 small) chicken breasts, sliced into thin strips to absorb the marinade and cook quickly

1 large green pepper, sliced

1 large onion, chopped into 8 pieces and layers separated

250g button mushrooms, stalks separated and tops cut into 4 quarters

240g brown rice

2 limes, outer zest grated and insides squeezed

Handful torn fresh basil leaves

1 tablespoon coconut oil

For the marinade:

4 garlic cloves, crushed

3cm root ginger, peeled and very finely chopped

1 heaped teaspoon Chinese 5-spice

2 limes, outer zest grated and insides squeezed

110 ml soy sauce

110 ml balsamic vinegar

110 ml olive oil

1 tablespoon honey

Method

1. Put the sliced chicken and marinade ingredients in a bowl, mix well, cover and place in the fridge for at least 4-5 hours (ideally, make it up the day before)

2. When ready to cook, take the marinated chicken out of the fridge and lift out the chicken pieces into a separate bowl. Set the bowl at a slight angle so the marinade juices flow to one side, hold the chicken pieces with a slotted spoon and pour the excess juices back in with the rest of the marinade. You need to get it as liquid free as possible so that it flash fries and cooks quickly in the frying pan or wok without boiling the meat

3. Pop a plate and a dish to warm in a 100 degree oven and then heat a large teaspoon of coconut oil in a large heavy based frying pan or wok. When the oil is starting to smoke, add half the chicken pieces and quickly spread out evenly over the pan using two wooden spoons so there is space between each piece

4. With the chicken thinly sliced, it will only take 2-3 minutes to cook on one side, browning the chicken and caramelising the marinade. Quickly flip all the pieces over and do the same to the other side, then lift out onto the plate in the warming oven. Add the second half of the chicken pieces and repeat. If you haven't got enough space in the pan, do it in three batches instead

5. There should be plenty of fat still in the pan. Add the sliced green peppers and stir-fry for 2 minutes, then add the onion and mushroom pieces and stir-fry for a further 3 minutes. Place into the dish in the warming oven

6. Pour the excess marinade into the hot pan, bring to the boil and simmer for 2-3 minutes until the consistency

becomes a syrup-like sauce, then add the sticky chicken and vegetables back into the pan, including all the juices, and give it all a final stir to coat the sauce around everything

7. Time the rice to be ready at the same time as the chicken and sauce (depending on the rice's cooking time). When the rice is drained, add the additional lime zest, juice and torn basil leaves, then serve with the sticky chicken

Rich's Taste Tips: Chopped red chillis are nice in the marinade if you like spicy food. You can also substitute the rice for cauliflower rice, which is cauliflower that has been steamed and simply mashed to resemble rice.

Back to Health Bonus: Having anti-cancer and anti-inflammatory benefits due to its high allium and quercetin content (nutrients found in it) onions are a must in any healthy eating diet. They also have high levels of vitamin C, B6 and manganese so help to boost the immune system and help good nerve function.

lemon sole with roasted root vegetables

Ingredients
(for 2 people)

2 pieces lemon sole

1 half head cauliflower, roughly chopped

2 large beetroot, roughly chopped

1 large sweet potato, skins on, roughly chopped

Juice 1 lemon

1 tablespoon coconut oil

Sea-salt

Method

1. Melt the coconut oil in a roasting tray with the oven at 200°C and toss the sweet potato and beetroot chunks in the oil, sprinkle with salt and roast for 20 minutes
2. Then toss the cauliflower chunks with the other veg and a little more salt, and cook for a further 20 minutes on a lower oven of 180°C
3. After putting the cauliflower back in, put the fish in a dish, squeeze over the lemon juice and place it beneath the veg on a lower shelf for the last 10-12 minutes
4. Remove the fish and the veggies and serve over 2 plates

Lou's Taste Tips: This tastes great with some lemon mayonnaise. So, put a couple of spoonfuls of mayo in a small pot, and mix in the juice of another ½ lemon.

Back to Health Bonus: Lemons are great for your immunity as they are full of vitamin C but they also acts as a major antioxidant in the body to combat damage from free radicals, the acid in them aids digestion and they help liver function. Use them in recipes or simply drink a slice squeezed into hot water each morning to boost your intake.

smoked salmon sauce with courgette noodles

This is such a quick and easy but tasty dish. Simply heat up the raw ingredients and serve immediately.

mins
prep time

Ingredients
(for 2 people)

300g cold smoked salmon (you can use off-cuts for this if you can find them – much cheaper!)

250ml coconut cream

2 tablespoons nutritional yeast flakes

3 tablespoons pine nuts

10 sun-dried tomatoes, finely chopped

Small bunch basil, chopped

4 spring onions, chopped

1 lemon, rind grated and squeezed juice

1 clove garlic, peeled, smashed, chopped and mashed with sea-salt

2 courgettes, spiralised or cut by hand into thin ribbons (thin slices lengthways then thinly slice each of those again lengthways – takes a bit of time!).

Method

1. Put all the ingredients except the courgette into a large frying pan and gently bring up to a simmer. As soon as simmering through, put the courgette in and toss through the sauce

2. Serve immediately and sprinkle with a little more basil

 Rich's Taste Tips: Again, fresh dill works with this instead of basil and you can throw 200-300g of small prawns in with the sauce to warm up.

 Back to Health Bonus: Pine nuts are yet another source of protein and are a great provider of monounsaturated fatty acids, magnesium and vitamin E, which are all great for a healthy heart.

garlic butter fish with strawberry salad

20 mins prep time

Ingredients
(for 2 people)

2 thick chunks any meaty, white fish (cod, haddock, hake, whiting or monkfish)

Plenty coconut oil

Sea-salt

2 large cloves garlic, peeled, crushed with the flat of a knife and roughly chopped

Any combination mixed salad leaves, 4 handfuls

6 decent sized strawberries, chopped into quarters

1 yellow pepper, chopped

4 spring onions, chopped diagonally

2 tablespoons white wine vinegar

3 tablespoons flax, rapeseed or olive oil

Salt and pepper to taste

Method

1. Put an oven proof dish or non-stick tray into the oven to heat at 180°C

2. Melt a large teaspoon of coconut oil in a non-stick frying pan on high heat, add two pieces of the fish and sprinkle with sea-salt. Fry very quickly on each side until starting to brown then lift off onto the warming plate in the oven. The reason for not cooking the fish all the way through in the frying pan is that it will flake and fall to pieces. Letting it finish cooking through in the oven will mean you can lift them carefully in one piece onto the salad

3. Whilst the fish is in the oven (about 10 minutes), toss all of the rest of ingredients (except the garlic) into a bowl and mix together. Arrange on four plates

4. Then put the frying pan back on a low heat with the fishy, salted cooking oil still in there (add a little more coconut oil if necessary so there's enough for drizzling over two fish) and throw in the chopped garlic. Gently fry for about 1 minute and then turn off the heat

5. Arrange the fish on top of the salad and pour over the garlic oil

Rich's Taste Tips: Torn up by hand, fresh dill tossed in with the salad really compliments any fish. Fresh coriander or basil also works well.

Back to Health Bonus: Flax oil (sometimes called linseed oil) is majorly anti-inflammatory as it is a huge source of omega 3 which we need to make good cell membranes forming the basis of all cell function. It's also very high in vitamin E which is another antioxidant used in the body to prevent tissue damage, particularly skin damage, so can help with healthy ageing.

thai fish curry

If you like curries, then you're going to love this one. In my opinion at least, this is one of the tastiest dishes that I cook and the one that I choose if I'm going to treat myself! To me, it's the perfect rich flavour combination of sweet, salty, spicy and fishy.

Ingredients
(for 4 people)

2 large pieces white fish which holds together well (monkfish tail is ideal) cut into about 2-3 cm square chunks

16–20 king prawns peeled and cooked (but you could use raw)

3 medium sized red chilli peppers (optional for heat!!)

2 heaped teaspoons Thai red curry paste (you can use green, but I prefer the red)

4 cloves garlic, peeled, crushed with the back of a knife and roughly chopped

1 tablespoon coconut oil

1 gluten-free fish stock cube or pot

1 tablespoon honey

400ml tin coconut milk

2 limes, grated zest + juice

1 large onion, peeled, halved, each half quartered and then separate the layers

1 large red pepper, deseeded and cut into large chunks

500g brown rice

Fresh coriander to garnish

Method

1. Put the rice on to cook depending on timing – brown rice usually takes about 25-30 mins, which is plenty of time to cook the fish curry if all the ingredients are chopped or grated in advance

2. Heat the coconut oil in a wok pan until hot and then add the chopped onion and pepper. Quickly stir fry for about 2 minutes and then spoon out into a bowl

3. Add more coconut oil to the hot wok and put in the garlic (and red chilli if adding). Fry for about 30 seconds stirring with a wooden spoon then add the Thai red curry paste and stir for a further 30 seconds

4. Turn off the heat and add the honey, then lime juice and zest along with the fish stock pot. Give it a little stir to cook off in the residual heat of the wok

5. Add the coconut milk and put the heat back on to bring up to the boil. Immediately add the fish chunks and simmer for 5 minutes until cooked then add the peeled prawns and stir fried onions and peppers. Bring back to a simmer and it will be immediately ready to serve at that point

6. Serve with the rice, sprinkled with fresh coriander and some sweet or spicy pickle on the side

Rich's Taste Tips: If you want to dial-up the heat on this, instead of using more chillis, use an Indian cookery trick I once learned, which is to add a couple of teaspoons of finely ground black pepper to fry off along with the chilli and garlic.

Back to Health Bonus: Chillis don't just add a bit of a kick in flavour they also add a huge vitamin C load to any dish. So, they help heal wounds, boost immunity, help relieve congestion, help tissue formation and help you to absorb iron from your diet.

monkfish chowder

mins prep time 20

Ingredients
(for 2 people)

2 large pieces monkfish tail, cut into chunks

16-20 king prawns, peeled and cooked (but you could use raw)

20-30 mussels, washed and de-bearded

1 large onion, peeled and chopped

1 sweet potato, chopped into small cubes

1 red pepper, deseeded and chopped

1 red chilli, deseeded and finely chopped

3 cloves garlic, crushed

1 teaspoon turmeric

1 gluten-free fish stock cube or pot

800ml (2 tins) coconut milk

Juice 1 lemon

1 teaspoon coconut oil

Handful fresh coriander

Method

1. Melt the coconut oil in a broad-based deep pan and fry off the chopped chilli for 30 seconds, then put in the chopped sweet potatoes. Stir and fry for 5 minutes until the potato cubes soften and then brown

2. Then add the onion, pepper and chopped garlic and fry off for another 5 minutes, stirring all the time before adding the turmeric and stock cube / pot. Give it a quick stir then add the coconut milk and monkfish chunks and bring to a simmer for 10 minutes to cook the fish through, but after 5 minutes, drop in the mussels

3. Finally, put in the prawns and lemon juice and warm through, then serve garnished with chopped coriander

Rich's Taste Tips: If you like seafood (and/or your head doesn't swell up like a balloon if you go near it, as with a close friend of mine), you can get creative with any kinds of seafood you want in this chowder: clams; crevettes; crayfish; squid; crab; or even lobster – just provide a bowl of water to wash fingers and another to throw away the shells!

Back to Health Bonus: Monkfish is a good source of low fat protein that also provides vitamins B6, B12 and selenium in decent quantities. It's not an oily fish so can't be counted as one of your weekly quota of omega 3's but its vitamins help with nerve function, selenium with low thyroid function and muscle growth / repair from the protein.

haddock with swedish creamy lemon sauce & butternut squash 'jenga' chips

*You can increase this by adding a green vegetable to the recipe

Ingredients
(for 4 people)

4 thick, short chunks haddock or any white fish

Butternut squash, sliced into 'Jenga' chips (see photo), 4 or 6 per person

Finely grated rind 3 lemons plus their juice

250ml coconut cream

1 gluten-free fish stock cube or pot

3 large cloves garlic, crushed

4 sprigs fresh parsley and pomegranate seeds to garnish

1 tablespoon coconut oil

Method

1. First of all put the coconut cream into a saucepan with the stock cube and crushed garlic and start simmering
2. Put the oven on to heat at 180°C with an oven-proof plate or non-stick tray
3. Then melt the coconut oil in a frying pan on medium heat and add the fish chunks. Fry off for about 2 minutes on each side then lift off onto the warming plate in the oven to finish cooking through which will take about 10-12 minutes
4. In the meantime, turn the heat down low and fry the jenga chips in the hot oil. 3 minutes on each side turning them as they brown should be enough to cook them through but not go too soft
5. As the final side of the chips are browning, add the grated lemon rind and squeeze the lemons into the sauce. It should have reduced to a thick creamy texture
6. Stack the jenga chips on warm plates, place the fish on top, drizzle with the lemon sauce and garnish with pomegranate seeds and fresh parsley

Rich's Taste Tips: You can use fresh dill or coriander, and also dried cranberries to garnish instead of parsley and pomegranate if you fancy a change.

Back to Health Bonus: Great on green salads or in rice salads, pomegranate adds a vitamin C, vitamin K, copper and folate boost to any dish. It shows anti-cancer, anti-inflammatory and blood pressure lowering capabilities. The juice is high in sugar though, so stick to the fruit!

gluten-free fish & chips

Ingredients
(for 2 people)

2 large pieces white fish, halved will make 4 smaller portions

2 large sweet potatoes, skins scrubbed and cut into chips

2 tablespoons coconut oil

2 heaped tablespoons gluten-free flour

2 tablespoons olive oil or flax oil

Juice 1 lemon

1 teaspoon smooth Dijon mustard

56ml unsweetened soya or almond milk (or you can use soda water for a Tempura style batter)

Sea-salt

Method

1. Melt half the coconut oil on a tray in a 200 degree oven, then add the chips and toss with salt. Put back in the oven for 20 minutes, take out and turn over, then return to the oven for a further 20 minutes

2. In the meantime, prepare the batter by adding the liquid oil (olive / flax) to the flour and stirring until it makes a paste. Then mix in the lemon juice, mustard and some more salt to taste. Finally carefully add in enough soya milk (or soda water) whilst stirring until the consistency becomes a creamy paste, but still thick enough to coat the spoon with a thick layer that will not substantially run off

3. When the chips have just 10 minutes left to cook, heat the rest of the coconut oil in a frying pan, then coat the fish with the batter and fry over a medium heat for about 4 minutes until golden brown on one side. Coat any excess batter on to the top of the fish with the spoon before turning and frying the other side. You can flip them another few times using available batter if required and frying for a further minute or two until golden brown on all sides

4. Serve with the chips, mayonnaise and you can maybe add mushy peas

 Rich's Taste Tips: I like to try to get other flavours into the batter than mustard and see how they pan out (if you'll pardon the pun!?). Things I have experimented with in the past are: finely chopped sun-dried tomatoes, gherkins or capers; or ½ teaspoon ground cumin, coriander, paprika or garam masala. They all give the batter a subtly different flavour to mustard.

 Back to Health Bonus: Almond milk is a great alternative to cow's milk, it contains fewer calories and is easier to digest. Just make sure you buy the unsweetened version so you minimise the effect on your blood sugar.

salmon with roast peppers & cauliflower

Healthy food doesn't have to be a pain to make and this recipe is a great example of that... Salmon is a brilliant source of protein that's also full of healthy fats and peppers are packed with vitamins to ensure you get a great meal that's quick and easy to make. Perfect!

mins
prep time

Ingredients
(for 2 people)

2 pavés (fillets sliced across) salmon

½ lemon

1 red pepper, deseeded and cut into strips

1 yellow pepper, deseeded and cut into strips

1 green pepper, deseeded and cut into strips

1 onion, quartered and separated

Sprig basil

½ head cauliflower

1 tablespoon coconut oil

2 large handfuls rocket

4 radishes

Black pepper

Olive oil

Balsamic vinegar

Method

1. Pre-heat the oven to 180°C and melt the coconut oil on a baking tray. Toss the peppers, onion and cauliflower in the oil and then roast in the oven for 20 minutes

2. After 5 minutes put the salmon in a dish, squeeze half a lemon over it and a little black pepper, then cook for 15 minutes with the vegetables

3. Take it all out, plate it up and put a sprig of basil on to garnish

4. Serve with a rocket and radish salad dressed with olive oil and balsamic vinegar

Lou's Taste Tips: You can actually use whatever veg you like. Red onions work well, as do courgettes or carrot. You will need to cook harder vegetables like carrot for longer, they need 40 minutes. Courgettes and red onions will take 20 minutes like the peppers.

Back to Health Bonus: Would you believe that black pepper helps to calm the digestive system preventing gas formation. It stimulates bile flow to help breakdown fat whilst also being high in manganese, vitamin K, iron and fibre. So, not just a seasoning!

moules marinières écossais

I first tasted a version of this in a French cafe in the charming city of Perth on the southern edge of the Scottish Highlands. It is an inspired combination, taking the classic French moules marinières recipe, but adding a touch of creaminess along with the intense flavour of a Scottish favourite, the Arbroath Smokie - smoked haddock from the fishing town of Arbroath, 40 miles away from Perth on Scotland's east coast. Over the years I've tweaked the recipe to what it is today.

Ingredients
(for 2 people)

500g fresh mussels in shells, beards removed and outsides swilled / cleaned (generally when you buy them from a supermarket or fishmonger they should come like this)

1 Arbroath Smokie, torn into small chunks

6 or 7 shallots or small onions, finely chopped

4 cloves garlic, crushed

2 tablespoons coconut oil

1 large sweet potato, skin scrubbed and cut into chips

200ml carton coconut cream

Handful chopped, fresh parsley

Juice 4 lemons

Coarse sea-salt and ground black pepper

2 gluten-free rolls

Method

1. Melt 1 tablespoon of coconut oil on a roasting tray before adding the sweet potatoes. Roast for 20 minutes then turn and cook for a further 20 minutes

2. Melt the coconut oil in a large, deep saucepan to which you can fit a lid. Add the chopped shallots / onions, crushed garlic and plenty of sea-salt and black pepper. Gentle fry off for 2-3 minutes until the onions are translucent

3. Add the mussels, coconut cream, lemon juice and small chunks of Arbroath Smokie. Give it a stir (or pop the lid on and toss) and put back on the heat with the lid on. Bring the liquid up to the boil and by the time the pan has steamed inside for about a minute, all the mussels should have opened their shells. Be careful not to overcook as the mussels will start to shrivel up

4. Throw in the chopped parsley and give the whole lot a final toss before placing on the table for everyone to help themselves. Serve simply with salted, sweet potato fries and some gluten-free rolls. But don't forget a spoon each for everyone to fight over the juices in the bottom of the pan like our kids do!

Rich's Taste Tips: Leave out the coconut cream and the Smokie, but add a little fish stock (150ml) and you have the classic moules marinières!

Back to Health Bonus: Being extremely high in vitamin K and high in iron, parsley is a great herb to throw in any dish. Most people have heard of vitamin K's involvement in good blood clotting but it's also essential for efficient use of calcium in the body, so if you're taking calcium supplements make sure you're getting enough vitamin K too!

caramelised onion, carrot & red-pepper omelette

40 mins
prep time

*Have this with a green salad to boost your veggie quota up to 3

Ingredients
(for 2 people)

1 large onion, peeled, halved and thinly sliced across in half-moon shapes

1 large carrot, peeled and finely chopped into small cubes

1 large red pepper, deseeded and sliced

3 teaspoons coconut oil

4 eggs

50ml almond milk

Pinch ground nutmeg

Small bunch fresh basil, chopped

Sea-salt and black pepper

Method

1. Using a fork in a jug or bowl, mix the eggs, milk, nutmeg and basil with some salt and pepper

2. Melt 1 teaspoon of coconut oil in a non-stick frying pan, add the onions and fry gently over a low heat for about 20 minutes, stirring frequently. They should eventually brown, caramelise and reduce. Set aside on a plate

3. Put the rest of the coconut oil in the pan with the carrot and red pepper and fry over a medium heat for 10 minutes stirring frequently

4. Add the onion and the omelette mixture back into the pan, turn the heat down and cook for 3 minutes. Loosen the edges and shake the pan to detach the underside of the omelette. Either flip over with a spatula, or pop the pan under a hot grill to cook the other side for 1 minute

5. Serve on its own or with some dressed salad leaves. Try olive oil and balsamic vinegar for your salad dressing

 Rich's Taste Tips: Use sweet potato instead of carrot and you get the classic Spanish omelette. You can also add chopped sun-dried tomatoes to the omelette mixture for a bit of a 'tanginess'.

 Back to Health Bonus: Just a little bit of nutmeg goes a long way. It's exceedingly high in a lesser known mineral called manganese which is needed for tissue and bone formation. It's also high in copper and magnesium which help your heart and decrease muscle cramps respectively.

imam bayildi (stuffed aubergines)

Ingredients
(for 4 people)

4 large aubergines

2 large onions, peeled and chopped

4 cloves garlic, peeled, smashed and finely chopped

10 sweet dates, stoned and finely chopped

3 medium tomatoes, chopped

Sea-salt and ground black pepper

Juice 1 lemon

Handful fresh flat leaf parsley, finely chopped

5 tablespoons coconut oil

5 tablespoons water

Method

1. Peel strips off the aubergines' skins lengthways with a peeler to make stripes (skin – peeled – skin – peeled, etc.). Cut each in half and sprinkle all sides with sea-salt. Set on a plate for 20 minutes for the salt to leach out some of the water then rinse off and dry. Cut a slit down the middle of each flat side stopping short of the ends or going all the way through to the skin side

2. Heat 3 tablespoons of the oil in a large frying pan or heavy saucepan to which you can fit a lid. Fry the onions over a gentle heat for 3 minutes, stirring until transparent. Add the garlic and fry for a further minute. Transfer into a bowl and mix with the rest of the ingredients except for the remaining coconut oil

3. Heat the remaining oil in the pan over a high heat and quickly fry to sear the aubergine halves on each side. Turn the heat off and spoon the mixture into the aubergine slits, stuffing as much in each as possible then putting the rest on top

4. Put the lid back on, turn the heat back on as low as possible and cook for about 40 minutes. Keep an eye it doesn't dry out and add a little more water if necessary. Allow to cool – it is traditionally eaten cold as a buffet dish or appetiser

Rich's Taste Tips: Add some finely chopped fresh chilli (red or green) to the onions for frying. The sweet and spicy go really well together.

Back to Health Bonus: Dates are full of fibre so good to prevent constipation but they also provide various minerals like magnesium, potassium and manganese needed for energy, good blood pressure control and normal nerve function.

stuffed portobello mushrooms

Recipe for 3 portobello mushrooms (we buy them in 3's at the supermarket).

50 mins prep time

Ingredients
(for 3 people or 1½ each for 2 people)

3 portobello mushrooms

3 cloves garlic, smashed with a flat knife and chopped

8 salted anchovy fillets in oil

2 tablespoons fresh thyme leaves (+ the soft stalks – separate from the "woody" bits)

2 teaspoons coconut oil

Sea salt

Black pepper

2 tablespoons nutritional yeast flakes

2 large handfuls mixed salad leaves

All finely chopped:

1 small red onion, peeled

1 carrot, peeled

½ stick celery

4 sun-dried tomatoes

The stalks of the 3 mushrooms

Method

1. Mash the chopped garlic and anchovy fillets in a pestle and mortar and then put on a low heat in a large based frying pan with a teaspoon of coconut oil. Stir and fry for about 4 minutes and the anchovy fillets should melt down and almost disappear (but leave a wonderful flavour!)

2. Then add more coconut oil, along with all the chopped ingredients, and the thyme leaves. Give it all a stir and turn down the heat to gently sauté for about 20 minutes, stirring occasionally until the mixture is thoroughly cooked and softened

3. Finally, stir in the nutritional yeast flakes and season with salt and pepper to taste. Then spoon the mixture into the Portobello mushroom cups on a baking tray, spreading the mixture out and flattening with the back of a spoon

4. Sprinkle a few more yeast flakes over the top, then put the tray into a 180⁰ oven for about 15-20 minutes. The mushroom cups will flatten themselves as they cook and the top of the mixture with the yeast flakes on should be a dark golden brown. Serve on a bed of salad leaves

Rich's Taste Tips: If you are just strictly gluten free and allowed some dairy, substitute the yeast flakes with a little bit of either crumbled or small chunks of creamy goat's cheese in and on this one.

Back to Health Bonus: Anchovies, are another oily fish which can be part of your 3 per week requirement to help maintain good skin and keep inflammation low. They also provide calcium so help with bone health too.

lentil & walnut salad

Ingredients
(for 4 people)

500g dried Puy lentils, soak for 3-4 hours if dried*

1 litre vegetable or beef gluten-free stock (home-made, pots or cubes)

3 garlic cloves, peeled, smashed and finely chopped

10 sun-dried tomatoes, cut into small strips

1 red onion, finely chopped

3 red peppers, deseeded and cut into strips

120g walnuts, chopped and toasted until lightly browned

1 handful parsley, chopped

1 handful mint, chopped

3 tablespoons olive oil

2 lemons, squeezed

1 tablespoon honey

1 teaspoon nutritional yeast

Salt & pepper

*Soaking removes phytates and saponins from the lentils. These make lentils difficult to digest, so the longer you soak them for, the better it is. I usually soak them overnight if I have the time.

Method

1. Put the lentils, stock and garlic into a large pan, bring to the boil and turn down to simmer for about 45 minutes. All the water should be soaked up or evaporated and the lentils soft, but still with a little bite. Transfer into a sieve and leave to go cold

2. For the dressing, mix together in a cup the olive oil, honey, lemon juice and season with salt and pepper

3. Toss the dressing together in a bowl with all the other ingredients, including the lentils, but not the nutritional yeast, which is for sprinkling on the top after serving

 Rich's Taste Tips: The garlic in this gets boiled to a mellow flavour in with the lentils and stock. I like to pep up this dish again by squeezing another very small clove into the dressing mixture. The raw garlic really goes well with the lentils.

 Back to Health Bonus: People underestimate the power of herbs and mint is no exception. It helps to promote digestion and ease wind by stimulating bile flow and relaxing muscles in your gut. It also contains fibre and small amounts of iron that boosts red blood cells.

asparagus & pea frittata

Ingredients
(for 2 people)

100g asparagus tips

200g garden peas

1 onion, finely chopped

1 teaspoon coconut oil

4 eggs

50ml almond milk

1 teaspoon coconut oil

½ teaspoon paprika

Sea-salt and black pepper

2 teaspoons nutritional yeast

Method

1. Using a fork in a jug or bowl, mix the eggs, milk and paprika with some salt and pepper

2. Fry off the onion in the coconut oil in a non-stick pan over medium heat for about 2 minutes until they soften and go transparent. Throw in the asparagus tips and peas, season with salt and fry for a further minute

3. Pour the egg mixture into the pan, turn the heat down and cook for 3 minutes. Loosen the edges and shake the pan to detach the underside from the pan. Either flip over with a spatula, or pop the pan under a hot grill to cook the other side for 1 minute

4. Finish off by sprinkling with nutritional yeast. Serve on its own or with some dressed salad leaves

 Rich's Taste Tips: If you're not intolerant/allergic to dairy a tasty little switch to this is goat's cheese instead of the nutritional yeast, add it after you've flipped it over before you pop it under the grill.

 Back to Health Bonus: Asparagus is a great source of folate needed to produce new cells so is vital for pregnancy. It's high potassium content acts as a natural diuretic so can help with water retention and the fibre in it helps to feed friendly bacteria in your gut. A great veg to get into your diet more often!

top tip

Goats dairy has a much smaller protein in it than cows dairy so can often be tolerated by those who need to be dairy free

sweet potato & lentil curry

*If on its own or 3 if with cauliflower rice (see below)

Ingredients
(for 4 people)

340g red or green lentils, soak for 3-4 hours if dried*

1 large onion, chopped

2 sweet potatoes, peeled and cut roughly into 1cm cubes

1 head cauliflower, roughly chopped

150g mange tout

2 heaped teaspoons curry powder (as mild or as hot as you like!)

2 heaped teaspoons turmeric

1 gluten-free vegetable stock pot or cube

400ml tin coconut milk

Juice 1 lemon

280ml water

*Soaking removes phytates and saponins from the lentils. These make lentils difficult to digest, so the longer you soak them for, the better it is. I usually soak them overnight if I have the time.

Method

1. Fry the onion until translucent then add the sweet potato cubes and occasionally toss

2. When the potatoes are starting to brown add the curry powder, turmeric and the vegetable stock cube. Stir and fry off the spices for another 30 seconds

3. Add the coconut milk, lemon juice, lentils and water. Turn down to simmer and stir occasionally to prevent sticking until the potatoes and lentils are cooked through and starting to break down. (You will start to get that curry sauce consistency – just keep adding a little more water if it starts to dry out too much before the potatoes and lentils are cooked and breaking up). This will take about 30 minutes

4. In the meantime, steam the cauliflower for 15 minutes and mash up into a rice. Steam the mange tout for 10 minutes. Serve on a bed of mashed cauliflower with steamed mange tout and (spicy) apple salsa (see Dips, Snacks and Finger Foods)

Rich's Taste Tips: I'm going to be weird again and say fruit in curry – don't know why it works but it just does! Dried cranberries, dried raisins, chopped apple or chopped mango – add for about 10 minutes before the end of simmering.

Back to Health Bonus: Lentils are a great source of protein and full of fibre and folate which help to balance blood sugar, keep you regular and help decrease your risk of heart problems.

veggie chilli

60 mins prep time

Ingredients
(for 4 people)

2 courgettes, cut into rough chunks

1 large red onion, cut into rough chunks

2 orange peppers, deseeded and cut into rough chunks

1 tablespoon coconut oil

400g tin kidney beans, drained

1 red chilli, finely chopped (leave the seeds in if you want it spicy)

400g tin tomatoes

500g carton of tomato passata

190g quinoa

1 gluten-free vegetable stock cube or pot

Mixed seeds (pumpkin, sunflower, sesame)

Sea-salt

500g brown rice

Method
1. Preheat the oven to 200°C
2. Roast the courgette, red onion and orange pepper with the coconut oil and a little salt sprinkled over them, in a tray for around 20 minutes until starting to brown
3. Put a little more coconut oil into a pan and briefly fry the chopped chilli for about 30 seconds to release the flavours
4. Add the roast veg, kidney beans, tomatoes, passata, quinoa and stock cube / pot. Bring to the boil and simmer for 20-30 minutes until the sauce has reduced to a thick paste
5. Whilst the chilli is reducing, put the rice on to cook for 20-25 minutes
6. Serve with rice and sprinkle with mixed seeds

Rich's Taste Tips: Top with either a blob of coconut yoghurt or guacamole – both go very nicely with chilli. Use the guacamole and this will also add to your veg quota for the day.

Back to Health Bonus: Full of protein, carbohydrates and fibre, kidney beans are a great addition to any meal, and that's not even mentioning that they also provide a multitude of minerals. However, if they are dried, they can be difficult to digest and contain substances that block the absorption of other nutrients. So soak them first and cook for a long time to try and prevent this and ease digestion.

stuffed sweet potatoes

Ingredients
(For 4 people)

4 sweet potatoes

4 tablespoons coconut oil

1 garlic clove, peeled and crushed

2 large shallots, finely chopped

400g tin chickpeas, drained

75g spinach

Handful dill, chopped

1 lemon, squeezed

Sea-salt

Ground black pepper

Topping – 20g pine nuts, 110g pomegranate seeds, sprinkled nutritional yeast

4 handfuls mixed salad, dressed with olive oil and balsamic vinegar

Method

1. Heat the oven at 140°C and wash and dry the sweet potatoes if they are dirty

2. On a tray scrape a little coconut oil around the skins of the potatoes and sprinkle all round with sea-salt, then put in the oven for 45 minutes

3. Meanwhile, in a frying pan, melt the rest of the coconut oil over a low heat and fry off the garlic and shallots for just two minutes then turn off

4. When the potatoes are cooked and crispy on the outside, take them out, cut in half and scrape out the soft centres into the pan with the garlic and shallots. Stir in the spinach to wilt in the heat of the potato, then add all the rest of the ingredients except the topping. Mix and season to taste

5. Spoon the mixture back into the eight potato skin halves, top with the nuts, seeds and nutritional yeast and put back in the oven for 10 minutes to warm through

6. Serve with dressed green leaf salad

Rich's Taste Tips: This has relatively subtle flavours as a main dish, so can also double as an accompaniment to something else.   However, you can always stir in stronger flavours to it like chopped sun-dried tomatoes, raw spring onions pieces or shredded, fresh basil leaves.

Back to Health Bonus: Chickpeas are a great source of plant based protein that makes you feel fuller and helps to control blood sugar levels whilst their high fibre aid digestion. However, take care as dried chickpeas need to be soaked for at least 12 hours before you cook them to remove toxins that block the absorption of other nutrients.

vegetable accompaniments

vegetable accompaniments

butternut squash dauphinoise

Watch out for this one as it has got goats butter in it. You can use the coconut oil we normally state to be strictly dairy free, but just beware it will make the dauphinoise quite oily.

Ingredients
(for 6 people)

1 large butternut squash, peeled and very thinly sliced

8 shallots, peeled and finely sliced

½ pack goats butter

8 cloves garlic, peeled, smashed and chopped

400ml carton coconut cream

Juice 1 lemon

½ teaspoon ground nutmeg

Sea-salt and black pepper

5 tablespoons nutritional yeast

Method
1. Set the oven to heat up at 140°C
2. Grind a generous amount of sea-salt onto the chopped garlic on a wooden board and mash with the back of a fork until you have a salty garlic paste
3. Then melt 2 tablespoons of the goat's butter in a frying pan over a low heat and gently fry the shallots for two minutes. Add the coconut cream, lemon juice and nutmeg, bring to a simmer and then immediately turn off the heat. Stir in the salty garlic paste
4. Layer up the thinly sliced butternut squash in a large oven proof dish by placing about ½ cm at a time. Spoon a small amount of the coconut cream mixture over, adding about 6 small teaspoons of butter and grinding over some more salt and black pepper
5. Finally, sprinkle the nutritional yeast evenly over the top and bake in the oven for an hour. Goes beautifully with red meat, e.g. our Duck Breast, Venison Stew or Fillet Beef recipes in the Main Meals chapter

Rich's Taste Tips: You can layer fresh parsley through this as you build it up and/or finely chopped red onions. It might, possibly, clash with your main dish tastes depending on what it is, so choose wisely.

Back to Health Bonus: Shallots contain sulphur needed for the liver to help detoxify toxins. They are also high in vitamin A and vitamin B6, which are needed for good immunity and for reproduction, to make hormones and to breakdown fat.

garlic & ginger kale

Ingredients
(for 2 people)

Large bag or bunch kale, chopped

3 cloves garlic, peeled, smashed and finely chopped

2cm root ginger, peeled and finely chopped

Sea-salt

1 tablespoon rice vinegar

2 tablespoon tamari soy-sauce

Large teaspoon coconut oil

Method

1. Heat the coconut oil in a wok or large frying pan over medium heat and add the garlic, ginger and a sprinkle of sea-salt

2. Stir and sizzle for 30 seconds, then turn up the heat to full and add the chopped kale. Toss the kale to coat it well with the garlic, ginger and oil

3. Keeping tossing and stir-frying for about 2 minutes until the kale leaves start to brown around the edges, then splash in the vinegar and soy sauce. Give it a last stir and serve

 Rich's Taste Tips: A bit of ground nutmeg (½ teaspoon) sprinkled in and tossed with the vinegar and soy sauce is a nice flavour which compliments kale (or any brassica veg – sprouts, cabbage, etc).

 Back to Health Bonus: A great little recipe, garlic, ginger and kale are all strongly anti-inflammatory so great for anyone with arthritis, or any other inflammatory condition. Just go easy on the tamari soy sauce though as it's pretty high in sodium which can affect your blood pressure.

savoury cauliflower rice

This can be used as an accompaniment, or eaten as a dish of its own. Just change the amount of cauliflower used and the additional ingredients to get the quantity you require.

Experiment with different combinations from each category to find your own preferred mixture.

20 mins prep time

Basic Ingredients
(for 4 people)

1 small head cauliflower

1 tablespoon flax oil or olive oil

1 tablespoon red wine vinegar

1 flat teaspoon paprika

1 flat teaspoon garlic powder

Salt and pepper to taste

Additional Ingredients

Add any combinations of veg, fruit and fresh herbs you want - raw and finely chopped:

• ½ red onion, 1 stick celery, 10cm length cucumber or courgette, small bag mange-tout, 1 pepper, 2 small chillis, 6-8 gherkins, 3 tablespoons capers

• 1 apple, orange or pear, 3 tablespoons dried cranberries or currants, 6-8 dried dates or apricots

• Small bunch fresh basil, coriander, parsley, chervil, dill or chives

Method

1. Chop the cauliflower into rough chunks and part-steam – about 8 to 10 minutes. You don't want to fully cook it, as it will still break up into small bits but leave it with a bit of "bite"

2. Mix with all the rest of the ingredients. Simple and tasty!

Rich's Taste Tips: This is in the veg section, but you can easily add small chunks of cooked or cured meat, fish or seafood to this such as chicken, duck, salmon or prawns.

Back to Health Bonus: Cauliflower is a cruciferous vegetable that is super important for liver detoxification and amazing for women who want to balance hormones and avoid menopause symptoms. It's also full of fibre and B vitamins so is an all-round great boost for your health!

ratatouille

Ratatouille can be eaten hot, but traditionally in France or Italy it is left to go cold and eaten as an accompaniment to meat or fish, or just on its own. In a café in Sorrento, I once even had a ratatouille sandwich (in the days when I wasn't gluten free obviously)!

80 mins prep time

Ingredients
(for 6 people)

2 large aubergines, chopped into 1 inch cubes

2 large courgettes, chopped into 1 inch cubes

2 large red onion, peeled and finely chopped

20 ripe plum tomatoes, coarsely chopped

5 cloves garlic, peeled, smashed and finely chopped

10 anchovy fillets

Small bunch fresh basil, finely chopped

2 tablespoons fresh thyme leaves, finely chopped

4 tablespoons coconut oil

3 tablespoons balsamic vinegar

3 tablespoons flax or olive oil

Sea-salt and black pepper

Method

1. Start by chopping the aubergines and courgettes and place the chunks in two colanders, generously grind sea-salt all over them. Toss them around and keep grinding on more salt until all the chunks are thoroughly coated

2. Leave them to stand for about 20 minutes while you chop the rest of the ingredients. The salt will 'leach' a lot of the water out of the vegetables. When this is done, thoroughly swill off all the salt under the tap and dry all the chunks between two clean tea-towels or kitchen roll in batches

3. Put 2 tablespoons of coconut oil in a large frying pan over a medium heat. Fry the aubergine chunks, stirring frequently, until the chunks are a little browned on the outside but soft and squishy in the middle. It will take about 10 minutes then set them aside on a plate. Repeat for the courgette chunks and also set aside

4. Add a further 2 tablespoons of coconut oil to the pan, along with the anchovies and garlic, and stir them. Fry the anchovy fillets until they break down and dissolve. Then add the red onion, basil and thyme. Fry for a further 5 minutes or so, also stirring frequently, until the onions start to caramelize

5. Finally, add the chopped tomatoes and cook them for 15 minutes until starting to break down into a sauce. Add the aubergine and courgette back into the pan, and when simmering, turn the heat down and let it cook slowly for a further 20 minutes

6. Right at the end, add the flax / olive oil and balsamic vinegar and stir them in

Rich's Taste Tips: I like to put capers through this for the last 20 minutes of simmering to give it extra saltiness. You can also add some more chopped anchovies.

Back to Health Bonus: A good source of fibre yet low in calories, aubergine is a great addition to any diet. It will help to keep you regular, is packed full of antioxidants that help prevent damage in the body and is high in potassium which helps to lower blood pressure.

pickled vegetables

When we lived for a time in France, our French friends used to host late afternoon / early evening 'dinetoire' parties, which roughly means nibbles. However, these nibbles usually amounted to a small buffet in their own right, and we always found we never then actually needed any dinner when we got home! A big feature of these spreads was always deliciously pickled vegetables to accompany whatever cold meats, fish or seafood that were on offer.

The beautiful thing about doing vegetables this way, is that they literally 'preserve' all of the vitamins, minerals and nutrients of the original vegetables, and keep them instantly accessible for up to 6 months without needing any further cooking.

You need large, sealing jars for this – either screw tops or metal spring clasps with a rubber seal. There are no quantities on this because you can do mixtures of different veg or just stick to a single ingredient, and it depends on the size of your jar(s). Just use your judgement for buying in and then fill as many jars as you want.

24 hours prep time

Ingredients

Sliced into ½ cm pieces, any mixture of the following, or you can do them individually:

Cucumbers

Peppers

Onions

Courgettes

Aubergines

Carrots

Fennel

Beetroot

Celery

Method

1. In large flat dishes or in pans, place some of the vegetables in a thin layer (basically only one piece thick of the ½ cm sliced veg) and grind sea-salt and sprinkle sugar over the layer. Continue building up in layers like this until you have filled the dish. Cover with cling film and put in the fridge for 24 hours. The salt and sugar will leach by osmosis through all the cells of the vegetables

2. After 24 hours, take the vegetables out of the fridge, swill off the salt and sugar under the tap in a colander or sieve. Do it in batches and allow to drain thoroughly before depositing in a separate dish

3. Sterilise the pickling jars using boiling water

4. Pour about a centimetre of white vinegar into the bottom of each jar, then spoon in about an inch of vegetables at a time, throwing in a little sliced garlic, rosemary, thyme and a bay leaf on each layer. Press down with a spoon, pour in some more vinegar until just covered, then give it a little swirl to release any air. Keep building up like this right to the top of the jar, give it a final swirl and then fill right to the top with vinegar

For the pickling and flavouring:

Sea-salt in a grinder

Granulated sugar

Garlic (as much or as little as you want), thinly sliced

Bay leaves

Fresh rosemary, leaves pulled off the stalks

Fresh thyme, leaves pulled off the stalks

White vinegar (not be confused with white wine vinegar)

5. Seal and let them sit for about 3 months in a cool place (larder, laundry, garage, shed) before using. They make lovely hors d'oeuvres or accompaniments to meat or fish

Rich's Taste Tips: Halve a couple of green chillies lengthways and pop them in the bottom of the jar at the beginning. The vinegar will extract the spiciness out of them over time and it will go right through the pickled vegetables.

Back to Health Bonus: This totally depends on which veggies you choose to pickle, however, whichever ones you do, getting more vegetables into your diet is great for your health as they contain antioxidants which protect the body against free radical damage caused by toxins, exercise or just living.

top tip

Goat's cheese is much easier to digest than cow's cheese. In fact, it takes only 20 minutes whereas cows cheese takes 2-3 hours! There's a reason why the old saying was to drink milk before you go out drinking, it literally lines your stomach and blocks everything else you have it with from being absorbed!

garlic salt roasties

*10 minutes preparation but 40 minutes cook time

Ingredients
(for 2 people)

Garlic salt (or fresh garlic 2 cloves, chopped & mixed with sea-salt)

1 tablespoon coconut oil

Any chunky cut root vegetable or combination of vegetables:

3 carrots, 1 large sweet potato, ½ medium butternut squash, ½ turnip, 3 parsnips, 2 medium onions, 1 fennel

(*there is a lot of garlic in this because we like it that way, decrease it down to 1 clove if you find it too much!)

Method

1. Melt a large teaspoon of coconut oil on a hot baking tray or oven proof dish and set the oven to 200°C

2. If using fresh garlic, grind a generous amount of sea-salt onto the chopped garlic on a wooden board and mash with the back of a fork until you have a salty garlic paste

3. Toss the chunky cut vegetables in the oil then sprinkle with garlic salt and toss again, or mix with the fresh garlic and salt paste

4. Roast for about 40 minutes tossing again halfway through until they start to brown and crisp around the edges

 Rich's Taste Tips: Rosemary and thyme are great herbs for roasting with. Finely chop the green leaves until you have a couple of tablespoons full, sprinkle over and toss in with the vegetables, oil and garlic salt at Step 3.

 Back to Health Bonus: The bonus here depends on which veg you're using. Whichever one you choose, extra veg in your diet improves gut function with the added fibre and boosts your antioxidant levels so eat up and enjoy!

courgette pasta

Ingredients
(for 4 people)

2 large courgettes

1 dessert spoon coconut oil

1 clove garlic

Method

1. Shred the courgettes using a grater or spiralise into thin strips if you have a spiralizer

2. Crush the garlic and leave it for 10 minutes for the active ingredients to work

3. Melt the coconut oil in a pan and add the garlic to it

4. Throw in the courgettes and fry off for 4-5 minutes before serving with your meal

 Rich's Taste Tips: Put a teaspoon of paprika in when you add the garlic to add some extra flavour.

 Back to Health Bonus: Courgettes are extremely low calorie but have good levels of vitamins C and A so won't bulk out your waistline whilst they help maintain good skin and mucus membranes.

dips, snacks & finger-food

dips, snacks & finger-food

You'll find no information on how many people the recipes in this section are for, as it totally depends how you are going to eat it! It could be a dip with others meant as a snack or part of a buffet, or meant for one person as a light lunch.

salmon & sun-dried tomato dip

Ingredients

213g tin wild salmon

3 sundried tomatoes

1 tablespoon mayonnaise

½ lemon squeezed

1 teaspoon paprika

½ clove garlic

1 tablespoon olive oil

Method

1. Put this all in a blender and switch on
2. Serve as a dip with veggie sticks or with gluten-free oatcakes

Rich's Taste Tips: Either using smoked paprika, ½ teaspoon ground nutmeg or some fresh dill all work very nicely in this dip.

Back to Health Bonus: Tinned wild salmon provides omega 3's, vitamin D via the bones and calcium, so is great to add into your diet, especially if you live in Scotland where sunshine is more sporadic. It's extremely anti-inflammatory so is great if you suffer from arthritis.

beetroot relish

Ingredients

1 fresh beetroot

4 tablespoons olive oil

1 teaspoon garlic salt

Sprinkle black pepper

½ lemon, squeezed

Method

1. Top and tail the beetroot, peel and then grate into a dish

2. Stir in the olive oil, garlic salt, black pepper and lemon juice

3. Serve with food or seal and store to have a spoonful with different meals during the week

 Rich's Taste Tips: Add some fresh coriander, finely chopped for about 1 tablespoon full, and stir through at Step 2 to pop in some extra flavour.

 Back to Health Bonus: This little recipe is a great helper to promote good liver function, as beetroot helps to dilate blood vessels, lemon stimulates digestive juices and black pepper boosts bile flow, all three of which aid your liver. Include this with any detox programme.

top tip

The health benefits from garlic are only produced after you chop or crush it, so leave it for 10 minutes before you cook it otherwise you'll stop this from happening.

lentil, red onion & turmeric dip

prep time 15 mins

Ingredients

300g red or green lentils

1 large red onion, peeled and finely chopped

½ clove garlic, peeled and chopped

1 heaped teaspoon turmeric powder

1 tablespoon coconut oil

2 tablespoons olive oil

Sea salt and black pepper to season

½ lemon's juice, squeezed

Method

1. If using dried lentils, soak in cold water overnight, then rinse thoroughly and boil in fresh water until soft and tender. This will take approximately 40 minutes

2. Heat 1 tablespoon of the coconut oil in a frying pan and fry the red onion and garlic for a few minutes until softened. Stir in the ground turmeric, salt and pepper, but turn off the heat immediately and keep stirring - the turmeric will cook and release its flavours in the residual heat

3. Put the cooked lentils in a blender with the olive oil, lemon juice and a bit more salt and pepper. Blend to a smooth paste, transfer to a bowl and stir in the onion, garlic and turmeric mixture. (Note: you can also blend the onion mixture or leave this in chunks within the dip)

4. Serve as a dip, on gluten-free oatcakes, or use a spoonful as a relish with fish or meat

 Rich's Taste Tips: You can make this one slightly differently by using 3 white onions and frying them on their own very slowly, for about half an hour, stirring regularly until they brown and caramelise. After that, add the garlic to fry for 1 minute and resume with the turmeric, etc. in Step 2.

 Back to Health Bonus: Salt has a bad reputation, but sea salt or Himalayan salt not only increase sodium levels, which is good if you're adrenally fatigued, but also boosts your magnesium, calcium and potassium, which are essential electrolytes needed to regulate your heartbeat and for good nerve conduction. Go easy though, even if you are adrenally fatigued you only need a little!

smoked mackerel paté

mins prep time

Ingredients

1 smoked mackerel
(Arbroath Smokie or similar)

Handful fresh dill

2 tablespoons mayonnaise

½ teaspoon garlic salt

½ teaspoon ground nutmeg

2 tablespoons olive oil or
flax oil

½ lemon, squeezed

Method

1. Put all ingredients into a food processor or using a hand-blender, blend to a smooth paste
2. Serve as a dip or on gluten-free oatcakes

 Rich's Taste Tips: Lime and fresh coriander give a different flavour to this than the lemon and dill, but equally pleasant.

Back to Health Bonus: You need to eat three portions of oily fish per week to maintain good skin, hair and help decrease inflammation. Mackerel is a great oily fish to eat regularly but try not to eat too much smoked as the nitrates produced from smoking can be detrimental to health.

green olive tapenade

mins prep time

Ingredients

200g green olives, pitted
(can also use black olives)

½ clove garlic

½ lemon squeezed

Method

1. Put this all in a blender and switch on – blend to a paste or leave slightly chunky
2. Serve as a dip with veggie sticks, on gluten-free oatcakes, or use a spoonful as a relish with fish or meat

 Rich's Taste Tips: Add as much salt and pepper to this as you like to taste. Or drop in an anchovy – goes very nicely!

Back to Health Bonus: Green olives are full of antioxidants (namely vitamin E, selenium and zinc) that help to decrease cell damage in the body and help combat inflammation due to their high good fat content.

salty &/or spicy nuts

I usually say roasted and salted nuts are dead and give you little in the way of nutrients. However, every now and then it's nice to enjoy a salted nut or two, so here's a way to enjoy them with less impact from the processing of bought nuts.

Ingredients

150g cashews, almonds or walnuts (or a mixture thereof)

3 tablespoons boiling water

1 flat teaspoon salt (or garlic salt is very tasty)

½ teaspoon honey

1 teaspoon paprika

And if you like them spicy, ½ teaspoon cayenne pepper

Method

1. Put a frying pan onto a high heat and throw in the nuts to dry fry. Toast them for about 2 minutes, tossing or stirring so they start to smoke and brown

2. Meanwhile, measure out the boiling water into a glass from the kettle and stir in the (garlic) salt, honey, paprika and the cayenne if spiciness is required

3. Throw the water / salt / spice mix into the smoking pan with the toasted nuts and the water will sizzle and quickly boil off. Toss or stir as this happens to coat the flavours and salt / sugar crystals around the nuts

4. Serve into a flat dish and allow to cool. With the honey in, the nuts may 'set' together as they cool. Simply break them up with a spoon

 Rich's Taste Tips: You can go for ½ teaspoon of ground cumin and/or ground coriander also in the water around these, to give them a slightly curried flavour.

 Back to Health Bonus: Cashews contain high levels of magnesium, manganese and copper which help to decrease the frequency of migraines, work to speed up reactions needed in the body and helps maintain a healthy heart respectively.

cauliflower nibbles

mins
prep time

Ingredients

1 cauliflower, chopped into small pieces

1 tablespoon coconut oil

2 tablespoons sunflower seeds

2 teaspoons garlic salt

Method

1. Melt the coconut oil on a tray in a 200 degree oven

2. Toss the cauliflower pieces in the oil with the garlic salt and then roast in the oven for around 20 minutes until browning all round. Stir more frequently in the latter stages to brown on all sides

3. Sprinkle sunflower seeds over the cauliflower and serve

Lou's Taste Tips: If you fancy something sweeter drizzle a tablespoon of honey over the cauliflower before you roast it. Sweet and salty always works well together.

Back to Health Bonus: Sunflower seeds are high in vitamin E which protects your cells from damage and is used for many organs to function well. Plus they're a source of good fats and protein, so what more can you ask for?

apple salsa

Ingredient

1 clove garlic

1 teaspoon garlic salt

1 tablespoon cider vinegar

Juice 1 lemon

1 tablespoon runny honey

1 teaspoon cayenne pepper
(if you want it spicy)

All finely chopped:

2 apples, peeled and cored

1 stick celery

1 cup walnuts

½ red onion

Small bunch fresh parsley

Method

1. Peel the garlic and smash with a flat knife before chopping it. Sprinkle with the garlic salt and mash to a pulp with the back of a fork on the chopping board

2. Scrape into a small bowl, add the cider vinegar, lemon juice and honey (and cayenne pepper at this point) with the rest of the chopped ingredients and give it a stir with the fork

3. Serve with meat or use it as a garnish with fish

Rich's Taste Tips: If you want this even more spicy you can add 1 chopped red chilli!

Back to Health Bonus: Cayenne can help to clear congestion, decrease pain from arthritis as it's highly anti-inflammatory, can improve blood sugar fluctuations (so help with type 2 diabetes) and can help prevent cancer. Caution though: a little goes a long way and too much can irritate your stomach!

top tip

You'll see no mention of pork in this book, as it's really inflammatory so anyone with any gut issue, joint pain or inflamed anything should avoid it. I'm not saying never eat it again, but rarely is the best way to go.

guacamole

mins prep time

Ingredients

3 ripe avocados, stoned, scooped out and roughly chopped

1 red onion, finely chopped

15 cherry tomatoes, finely chopped

Bunch fresh coriander, chopped

1 clove garlic

2 teaspoons paprika

Juice 1 lime

1 teaspoon runny honey

3 tablespoons olive oil

1 teaspoon sea-salt

Black pepper

Method

1. In a pestle and mortar, grind up the garlic clove, sea salt and about half of the chopped coriander

2. Squeeze in the lemon juice, add the olive oil and then using a teaspoon, scrape the garlic and coriander away from the walls of the mortar and empty into a larger bowl. (Note: if you have a very large pestle and mortar, you can mix the whole thing in there rather than transferring to a bowl)

3. Add the paprika, honey and chopped avocados, then mash and mix with a fork until you get a reasonable paste, but still with some avocado chunks in it

4. Finally, mix in the chopped onions, cherry tomatoes and the rest of the chopped coriander. Season to taste with more sea-salt and black pepper

5. Serve as a relish with Mexican food or use as a dip

Rich's Taste Tips: If using as a dip or relish, you can add ½ teaspoon of cayenne pepper or a few chopped jalapenos to "pep-up" a little if required. Guacamole is however, usually the smooth, cool, non-spicy accompaniment to other hotter Mexican food.

Back to Health Bonus: Full of good fats, loaded with fibre whilst extremely high in vitamin K, folate, vitamin C, B5, B6 and potassium avocado really packs a punch. Put it in salads, eat with prawns and tomatoes or simply put it on gluten-free toast to get this superfood into your diet more often.

mango salsa

10 mins prep time

Ingredients

1 clove garlic

Sea salt

Juice 1 lemon

Juice 1 lime

All finely chopped:

½ ripe mango, peeled and stoned

½ yellow pepper, seeded

6 cherry tomatoes

¼ red onion

Small bunch fresh coriander

Method

1. Peel the garlic and smash with a flat knife before chopping it. Sprinkle with sea salt and mash to a pulp with the back of a fork on the chopping board

2. Scrape into a small bowl, add the lime and lemon juice with the rest of the chopped ingredients and give it a stir with the fork

3. Serve on a turkey burger (see the meat dish section) with a gluten-free roll or just use as a dip for gluten-free naan or veggie sticks

Rich's Taste Tips: Traditionally you'd use this as a relish but it's also really tasty with fish!

Back to Health Bonus: One portion of mango provides your daily requirements of vitamin C, needed for a good immune system, and a third of your daily vitamin A, needed for good vision and to maintain good gut membranes.

classic green tomato salsa (salsa verde)

If you cannot buy green tomatoes in the supermarket, see if you know anyone who grows tomatoes in a greenhouse or conservatory. They generally need to prune off smaller, green fruit through the season, from bunches of three in order for the rest to ripen and get bigger. However, these unripe fruit have a very strong taste, even when still green, particularly when complimented by the right additional flavours as in this recipe.

Ingredients

7 or 8 green tomatoes, finely chopped

½ red onion, finely chopped

2 tablespoons pickled jalapeno peppers, finely chopped

½ teaspoon cayenne pepper

½ teaspoon paprika

½ teaspoon ground cumin

Large handful fresh coriander, chopped

Juice 2 limes

1 tablespoon honey

1 large garlic clove

1 teaspoon garlic salt

Method

1. Peel the garlic and smash with a flat knife before chopping it. Sprinkle with the garlic salt and mash to a pulp with the back of a fork on the chopping board

2. Scrape into a small bowl. Add the chopped jalapeno, cayenne, paprika, cumin, lime juice and honey, and give it a quick stir for the juices to absorb and 'cure' the spices. Then add the rest of chopped ingredients and thoroughly stir to coat everything together

3. The salsa is lovely with Mexican food but can also make a dip and goes nicely with different fish dishes

 Rich's Taste Tips: Fresh basil works well with this instead of the fresh coriander. Tomato and basil is a classic combo.

 Back to Health Bonus: Cumin is a powerful spice that aids digestion by stimulating the flow of bile and improving the activity of digestive enzymes needed to breakdown food. It's also a good source of iron needed to combat fatigue.

desserts

desserts

I would say 'everyone loves a dessert' but, actually, Richard's not that keen unless it is coffee flavoured! Anyway, a recipe book wouldn't be complete without a few things to tempt your sweet tooth and, let's face it, sticking to any eating plan, healthy eating or not, is difficult unless we have something sweeter on occasion. So, here's a few recipes that you can enjoy without the guilt as they won't damage your healthy goals.

blueberry muffins

Ingredients
(makes 6-8 muffins)

440g gluten-free flour

110g honey

3 eggs

½ teaspoon baking powder

1 teaspoon vanilla extract

5 tablespoons coconut oil

140g frozen blueberries

Method
1. Preheat the oven to 180°C
2. Mix together coconut oil, eggs, vanilla and honey in a mixing bowl
3. Slowly add the flour and baking powder to this mixture, stirring frequently to avoid lumps
4. Use a little more coconut oil to grease a muffin tray
5. When the mixture is well mixed, add the frozen blueberries before separating it out between the individual muffin bays
6. Cook in the oven for about 25 minutes

Lou's Taste Tips: If you fancy a change you could use frozen cherries in this recipe too or, indeed, any frozen berry works well. Have a play about with it and find your favourite!

Back to Health Bonus: Blueberries are a powerhouse of goodness! Bursting with antioxidants which prevent cell damage and reduce the signs of ageing whilst also being full of fibre that helps to reduce cholesterol, so they're a must in any diet!

banana bread

Ingredients

4 bananas, mashed

4 eggs

2 tablespoons gluten-free flour

1 tablespoon cinnamon

1 teaspoon baking soda

1 teaspoon gluten-free baking powder

2 tablespoons almond or cashew butter

4 tablespoons coconut oil

1 teaspoon vanilla

Small sprinkle sea-salt

Method

1. Preheat the oven to 180°C

2. Put the bananas, eggs, coconut oil and nut butter into a blender with the flour, cinnamon, baking soda, baking powder, vanilla and sea salt. Mix them all together until they make a smooth paste

3. Grease a baking tray using a little more coconut oil then pour the mixture onto it. Spread it in an even layer

4. Cook for 55-60 minutes or until a knife inserted into the centre comes out clean

5. Cool it and cut into slices before eating

 Lou's Taste Tips: If you're a nut lover, walnuts go really nicely in this. I would smash them up first and add them to the blender with the rest.

 Back to Health Bonus: Cinnamon is brilliant to help balance your blood sugar so can help to prevent cravings and be a help if you're trying to lose weight. Add it to flapjack, stewed apple or sprinkle on muesli or porridge to get it into your diet.

fruit sorbet

15 mins
prep time
(then 5.5 hrs)

Ingredients
(for 4 people)

200ml boiling water

185g honey

Juice 1 lemon

250g fresh mango or strawberries

Method

1. Combine the water and honey in a small saucepan. Bring to the boil over a medium heat, and stir to fully combine then allow to cool completely

2. Purée the lemon juice, chopped fruit and honey syrup in a blender until smooth. Taste and add extra juice or honey, if desired

3. Pour the mixture into a shallow lidded container, cover and freeze for about 3 hours, or until a firm ring of ice appears around the sides and base, and there is a soft slush in the centre

4. Transfer to an electric mixer or food processor and beat until smooth. Return to the freezer until firm, then beat and freeze 2 more times

Lou's Taste Tips: You can make this with any fruit you like or any combination of fruit.

Back to Health Bonus: Mango is high in vitamin C and A so is great to prevent colds and help with good eye health. But, watch out though, its high sugar so it's not something to eat too often!

coconut crème brulée

40 mins prep time

Ingredients
(for 4 people)

3 tablespoons honey

8 large free-range egg yolks

500ml coconut cream

Method

1. Preheat the oven to 180°C
2. In a bowl, whisk the honey into the egg yolks
3. Pour the cream into a saucepan and gently heat the coconut cream until it is just below boiling point
4. Pour the heated cream onto the yolks and whisk together
5. Pour into 4 x 150ml ramekins or shallow brûlée dishes
6. Put the dishes into a baking tray and pour enough just-boiled water from the kettle to come halfway up the sides of the ramekins. Bake for 20-25 minutes until set but with a slight wobble
7. Remove from the baking tray and leave to cool, then put in the fridge and chill before serving

Rich's Taste Tips: Put in a fresh vanilla pod, split in half, to heat up with the cream and then lift out before combining with the yolks (but scrape out the seeds and put them back in).

Back to Health Bonus: Although coconut cream is high in fat it is also highly anti-bacterial and anti-fungal due to its lauric acid content. Its benefits don't stop there as it's also high in iron, phosphorus, copper and manganese so helps reduce fatigue and maintains good bone health.

lime cheesecake

20 mins prep time

Ingredients
(makes 8 small ramekins)

For the base:

150g ground almonds

150g Medjool dates

4 tablespoons coconut oil

For the top:

400g raw cashews, soaked overnight

500ml coconut cream

65ml maple syrup

Juice and zest 3 limes

1 lime*, juice only (therefore 4 limes needed in total)

1 square dark chocolate

*keep 2 slices of lime back for a little decoration

Method

1. Put the ground almonds and dates with the coconut oil into a blender and whizz them all up

2. Divide the mixture between the 8 ramekins and press it down into a firm base

3. Place the ramekins into the freezer for 30 mins

4. Next, clean the blender before putting the cashews, coconut cream, maple syrup and lime juice / zest into it

5. Whizz them up and then divide the mixture between the eight ramekins and place them back in the freezer for 2-3 hours

6. Remove about an hour before eating so that they start to defrost but are still cool and firm when eaten

7. Decorate with a small piece of lime and a little grated dark chocolate over the top

 Lou's Taste Tips: This recipe works just as well with lemons if you prefer!

 Back to Health Bonus: Dark chocolate doesn't just taste lovely, it's good for you too! Full of antioxidants to mop up damage in your body caused by toxins plus multiple minerals needed to boost vital bodily functions.

banana chocolate sticks

40 mins prep time

Ingredients

2 bananas

100g dark chocolate

200g pistachio

Method

1. Slice a banana diagonally across to give you the maximum surface area, and cut again about 1 cm away from the first cut to give you a generous slice

2. Push a lolly stick into the banana lengthways and put the lollies into the freezer on a tray

3. Leave for 4 hours

4. Whilst they are freezing shell the pistachios and crush up into small bits (wrap them in a clean tea towel and bash them with a rolling pin)

5. Melt the dark chocolate in a glass bowl placed on top of a pan filled with boiling water

6. Remove the banana lollies from the freezer and dip them into the chocolate, then roll them into the crushed pistachios

7. Put them back into the freezer on the tray to solidify

8. Remove them when you're ready to eat them

Lou's Taste Tips: You can easily switch pistachios for pecans if you prefer a change.

Back to Health Bonus: A great source of protein plus full of calcium, magnesium and a huge number of vitamins, pistachios are a real powerhouse of nutrition. Great for sprinkling on salads, porridge or just enjoying on their own!

berry mousse

Ingredients
(for 4 people)

450g cashews, soaked overnight

250g mixed frozen berries

3 ripe bananas

2 tablespoons honey

225ml chilled almond milk

Fresh mint leaves to garnish

Method

1. Put the cashew nuts in a bowl and cover them with water overnight

2. Remove the cashews from the water and put them in a blender with all of the other ingredients and whizz them up

3. Put it in the fridge until eating

4. Garnish with a piece of mint

 Lou's Taste Tips: The creaminess and sweetness of this mousse comes from blending bananas with cashew nuts which have been soaked in water. If you're not keen on the mixed berries selected here you can swap them for any type of individual berries: blueberries, blackberries, raspberries, strawberries or any combination.

 Back to Health Bonus: Almond milk is a great alternative to cow's milk, being high in calcium and protein yet free of lactose and hormones. It's full of good fats so can be considered anti-inflammatory too!

apple flapjack

mins
prep time

Ingredients

2 large apples, peeled and chopped

1 tablespoon water

½ lemon squeezed

120g cranberries

180g oats

2 teaspoons cinnamon

3 teaspoons coconut oil

Method

1. Preheat the oven to 180°C
2. Use 1 tablespoon of coconut oil to grease a baking tray
3. Peel and chop the apples and place in a pan with about one tablespoon of water and some lemon juice, and let it simmer until soft and turning into mush
4. Remove the pan from heat and add the cranberries and the cinnamon
5. When the cranberries start to enlarge as they absorb the juices, add the oats, two tablespoons of coconut oil and mix them together. Make sure that there are no lumps of coconut oil left. If you think the oats have soaked up all of the coconut oil and are still a little dry, add another tablespoon otherwise your flapjack may turn out rather crumbly!
6. Spoon the mixture into the baking tray and press down to compact it firmly
7. Cook for about 25 minutes until it goes lightly brown
8. Remove from the oven and leave to cool
9. Cut up to whatever size you'd like them to be

 Lou's Taste Tips: If you're not a cranberry lover you can always switch them for raisins to make a more traditional flapjack.

 Back to Health Bonus: Cranberries are high in fibre and antioxidants which combat damage in the body caused from everyday living. They're a really great addition to salads or can be eaten as a snack but, beware, they are high in sugar. So, shop carefully and find the ones which are infused with pineapple juice so at least it's natural sweetness!

coconut chocolate mousse

10 mins prep time

Ingredients
(for 4 people)

320ml coconut cream

½ teaspoon vanilla essence

3 tablespoons raw cacao powder

4 tablespoons honey

Method

1. Empty the contents of the coconut cream carton into a bowl
2. Add the vanilla, honey and cocoa powder to the bowl
3. Whisk them all together for 2-3 minutes to ensure there are no lumps, and the mixture starts to thicken
4. Separate the mixture into 4 small ramekins and put them in the fridge to chill for 3 hours
5. To serve, add three or four raspberries to the top and grate dark chocolate over them if you like!

Lou's Taste Tips: If you're a nut lover flaked almonds work well on this too. You can either add them to the raspberries or have them on their own sprinkled on the top.

Back to Health Bonus: While I appreciate it's difficult to extrapolate health benefits from all desserts you can rest assured that this is way better for you than any shop bought mousse. Coconut contains saturated fat but it is used immediately as energy and not stored. Honey is a natural sugar that your body can process and there are no artificial preservatives. So, if you fancy chocolate mousse, this is the best way to go!

chocolate brownies

25 mins prep time

Ingredients

For the brownies:

1 medium sweet potato, grated

2 eggs

3 tablespoons melted coconut oil

2 tablespoons honey

2 teaspoons vanilla extract

3 tablespoons raw cacao powder, sifted

1 teaspoon gluten-free baking powder

1 teaspoon baking soda

2½ tablespoons gluten-free flour

For the raspberry jus:

1 punnet raspberries

2 tablespoons water

1 tablespoon honey

Method

1. Preheat oven to 180 °C
2. Mix grated sweet potato, eggs, vanilla, honey and coconut oil in a large mixing bowl
3. Add cacao powder, baking powder plus baking soda and stir
4. Add the flour and mix in – watch the consistency here as too much flour will dry them out
5. Use extra coconut oil to grease a baking tray. Pour the mixture onto the greased baking tray
6. Cook for 25-30 minutes
7. Whilst it is cooking make the raspberry juice – take 3/4s of the raspberries, add the water and the honey and blend them up
8. When the brownies are ready, let them cool before cutting them into squares and sprinkle a little cacao powder over them
9. Serve with raspberries and the jus

Lou's Taste Tips: You can easily substitute strawberries for raspberries or blueberries if you prefer.

Back to Health Bonus: With a higher antioxidant level than dark chocolate and more than 20 times that of blueberries, you can see why raw cacao is good for you. It helps fight damage caused to the body by stress, pollution and everyday chemicals.

peach crumble

This is a lovely crumble that can be made with peaches or supplemented for any fruit that you like.

Ingredients

280g oats

3 tablespoons coconut oil

1 teaspoon vanilla extract

1½ tablespoons maple syrup

5 peaches, washed, destoned and sliced

Method

1. Preheat the oven to 180°C
2. Put the oats in a bowl
3. Add the coconut oil and use your finger tips to massage it into the oats, just like you would with butter and flour
4. Add the vanilla and maple syrup, and massage these in too
5. Put the peaches in the bottom of a dish and add three tablespoons of water to keep them moist
6. Cover them with the oat topping
7. Cook for 35 minutes until the oats are lightly browned

 Lou's Taste Tips: You can switch out the fruit if you're not keen on peaches. Pears or apples are a good substitute. Peaches are sweet though so you may need to add a little honey to apples to sweeten them up a bit.

 Back to Health Bonus: Peaches are a great source of fibre to help keep you regular, contain antioxidants that help keep your skin looking good and are packed full of minerals. An all-round great fruit to have regularly in your diet.